A Journey from Death to Life

SALEM'S GATE

A Journey from Death to Life

SALEM'S GATE

DONALD DAVID SIMS

PALMETTO
PUBLISHING
Charleston, SC
www.PalmettoPublishing.com

Paperback ISBN: 979-8-8229-4447-3
eBook ISBN: 979-8-8229-4448-0

Dedication

I dedicate this book to my late parents: my father, Dr. Oliver Hoke Sims, and my mother, Floy Belle Silver Sims. For many reasons, they deserve to be honored. Having brought myself and six other children into the world to feed, clothe, and educate, I am indebted to their legacy of love, faith, and aspirations. My parents' influence lives on in the narrative of this book, *Salem's Gate*.

Further, I wish to mention my wife Rhonda, who has essentially typed and edited my work. Her love and that of my daughter, Lorin, a dedicated caretaker, and my son, David, who practices optometry (as did my father), have supported me during this journey.

I also credit my friend, David Brown, who gave me significant encouragement to complete this book when I needed a push forward.

Contents

THE

GATE OF

SALEM

RAVAGED

King Akaan Invades Salem

High from the ridge, the rider peers across.
Elaam has ridden since sunrise; now halts.
He partakes of the wine and fruit he brought.
The horse uproots the crisp grass glazed with frost.

Elaam pensively views the scene below,
The raid on Salem evidenced by smoke.
As King Akaan ordered, Elaam must go,
Prince Necor has armed him lest he meet foes.

Akaan, sagacious, well advised, and shrewd,
Thus orders Elaam to proceed as sleuth.
For such endeavors, covert means are used
To save the treas'ry from those who would loot.

King Akaan's five Princes hear the King speak,
"I adjure by the gods and their winged speed,
Go ye and war on Krislos, I charge thee,
Spoil Salem and the land, bring his defeat.

See to it, ye Princes," the King implores,
"That Krislos' infidels meeting thy hordes
Last recollect the honed shafts of thy swords,
But save his skin that I may pick it sore.

Erstwhile, assault continues on the church.
The Saints are being slaughtered, great the purge.
Throughout the holy nave, the raiders search,
Looting and stripping everything of worth.

A very frightened girl hides in a room,
Nearly hysterical as dangers loom.
The sound of footsteps comes; she senses doom.
Evincing beauty, she's in youth's full bloom.

Elaam follows a map to the stored wealth,
Bejeweled splendor on his right and left,
Gems shimmer, multifaceted indwelt
Of brilliant radiance, in mountings kept.

He puts scrolled inventory in an urn,
Inserts the lid well-secured with a turn,
Seals the top tightly as the wax becomes firm.
He snuffs out the lamps and makes his return.

Elaam ties his horse near the temple gate,
Crosses the marble terrace toward the nave.
The mammoth temple doors, standing agape,
Engulf him, as might the mouth of a cave.

He is soon addressed and identified,
Led to quarters Bomar now occupies.
With the best of wine, Bomar is well-supplied,
Drunk, obnoxious, and filled with heady pride.

The girl there, captive, writhes in searing pain.
Her eyes are swollen shut. She pleads in vain
That the officer on her be restrained.
Finishing, he takes her cross and gold chain.

Elaam reacts with sympathy for her,
For this heedless abuse has struck a nerve.
His first impulse is to attempt to save her.
He thinks of a scheme, which he shall assert.

Bomar's officers escort Elaam in.
They announce Elaam's name, presenting him.
Bomar then raucously shouts o'er the din,
"Behold him, 'the eyes' of Necor the Prince!

Elaam, now thou seest Rabac's 'right arm'
That smiteth the infidel, fief, and farm.
With mighty hand, as vengeful hornets swarm,
I inflict on this people lasting harm."

Elaam's desire to be briefed on the raid,
To gather new facts from Bomar, fast fades.
Buffoonery reigns, disaster is praised,
Elaam thus his own appraisements shall make.

Does Bomar know of Elaam's very quest,
Of Elaam's coming at Akaan's behest?
If so, Elaam may be followed at best,
Or Elaam's will to live put to the test.

He may need an accomplice for his goal
To take the scrolls to Akaan undisclosed.
For he sees the clear danger that is posed
From those who would for gain usurp his role.

Elaam replies, "So ye've vanquished this girl!
Thy garrisons subdue tresses and curls.
Rise, fools, find thy wits, get ye dice to hurl.
I shall rob thy pockets of pelf and pearls."

They laugh, "Show what thou hast to risk and lose?"
Elaam threw a cloth on the floor of the room
On which he spread jewels and gold doubloons.
"See, swine, I've led a proper raid or two.

What ye possess," said Elaam, I seek.
Some temple spoils, and the young wench to keep.
Her cross I'll have, and my choice of a steed.
Now choose one of ye to gamble with me."

Thus, Bomar and the officers draw straws.
Rau is the one at the top of the draw.
Elaam and Rau vie, becoming enthralled.
They gamble so that the winner takes all.

Bomar and the others root loudly for Rau;
Curses at Elaam continue throughout.
Hard drinking is rife; they begin to pass out.
Rau seems to be winning the gaming bout.

Rau, clearly in the lead, with the last dice tossed.
The gaming concludes: Elaam has lost.
Rau beams at the take, at Elaam's great loss.
Elaam still plots for the girl, though distraught.

"Rau, I will give thee this dagger of mine
For an hour with the tart and some wine,
And we shall have some privacy assigned."
Rau accommodates, departs for the time.

Elaam finds clothing for her, which he brings,
Outfitting her even down to her feet,
Thirst is quenched with all the wine she will drink.
He retrieves her cross from the boor asleep.

He must gain her trust, help her understand
That quickly, he must take her from their hands.
Her injuries add challenge to his plan,
And more trauma, alas, she must withstand.

He asks her pointedly, "What is thy name?"
Her lips, once thin and delicate, now strain,
So swollen, she attempts some words to frame,
Makes syllables, which seem to her most strange.

"Thou, Rebekah, wilt die if I leave thee!
I must take thee from these men, set thee free.
Up! We cannot delay! Go thou with me,
I shall get thee a horse on which to flee."

It is torture for her to have to walk.
But her freedom, above all else, is sought.
She's animated by what hope has wrought,
And desperate to escape the assaults.

So Elaam leads her through the corridors,
On past the narthex, checking other doors.
He finds an exit to the rear, the north,
Having her wait until he finds a horse.

Rau now realizes he has been deceived.
Bomar, by fiat, shall thus be aggrieved.
The true loss unrelated to belief,
Enormous pride would nothing e'er concede.

Elaam has added more to the offense,
Obtaining a white horse on false pretense,
A stately steed of beauty led from thence,
From royal stables held by Bomar's men.

Rebekah shivers in the dark and cold,
Nervously waiting as events unfold,
Yearning to escape her cursed world of woes,
Alas, not knowing what the future holds.

The hours pass till morning quiet reigns,
Her feverish body small strength has gained.
With bruises deep, she is greatly restrained,
But rises to her feet despite the pain.

As Elaam has not yet returned for her,
Doubt of her escaping works cruelly its work,
To vacillate twixt hope and none, the worse.
Numb hopelessness seems to be preferred.

She sinks deep in despair and disbelief,
Then, uncontrollably, she sobs and weeps.
Depression encroaches via her grief,
She falls into a semiconscious sleep.

Belatedly, a hearty pilgrim came,
Who'd journeyed a great distance, preordained,
That he should travel thus as he maintained
To make his vows to God in this domain.

The ruin is shocking; he stands there appalled.
He climbs through the debris along the wall
And presses through the gate by merchants' stalls,
Then makes his way into the worship hall.

The slaughtered saints lie strewn, a cold dispatch.
He is repulsed and sickened by the fact.
Then he vows retribution for the act.
A faint disturbance stops him in his tracks.

He inquires, "Say thou, who doth go there? Speak!"
He waits for a reply with sword unsheathed.
He then steps forth but cautiously proceeds,
While corpses stare and for interment plead.

The girl recoils with fear from what she heard,
Yet hopes the man has now returned for her.
Warily, she speaks, slowly does emerge.
She peers up at the saint; their glances merge.

"I am a pilgrim, child, be not afraid.
Thou art alive, I see an act of grace."
"But sir, grace doth treat me in heinous ways,
Both life and death inhabit me today."

"Child, I perceive that thou hast welcomed one.
Lest I neglect to tell thee, I am John."
"I'm Rebekah, and a woman I've become.
A child I wast, in one night she hath gone.

My kinsmen here art dead, I beg thine aid.
I have no strength to bury them today.
If thou must leave, then please do not delay,
For by some means, I shall devise a way."

John says, "Find them, their graves I shall address.
Sleep thou and garner strength, relieve thy stress.
Whilst thou art in the quiet of recess,
Thy relatives shall then be laid to rest."

Rebekah finds a pool in which to bathe,
Housed in an edifice with colonnades.
A fountain feeds the pool in which she wades.
She plunges deep below a cool cascade.

Now, scores of cuts and bruises on her show.
The injuries felt even to the bone,
Yet, though in form, her elegance is shown
As she grooms splendid tresses with a comb.

The bath is very soothing to her skin.
A stain she cannot purge is felt within,
Which, scrupulously, she attempts to cleanse.
She promptly dons her clothing, sashed and pinned.

Latent rage erupts; her scream loudly rings,
She strikes her head until it bleeds and stings,
She wrecks the water urns and holy things.
Anger reverts to weeping, moody swings.

She sees the contradiction that is done,
For she recalls the very words of John,
Sleep thou, relieve thy stress whilst I am gone.
She laughs hysterically for moments on.

Unaware, Rebekah Enters the Reliquary

Exhaustion overcomes her as for spite.
She yields to rest and, taking John's advice,
Thus enters an open room aside,
She finds a tapestry on which she lies.

As she has entered by coincidence,
Scarcely does she observe the room's contents,
Noticing not sacred relics within,
The cross of St. Laud, the Shroud of Turin.

Oblivious, she grasps the linen shroud,
Drawing the cloth about her for a wrap,
Disproportionate peace comes like a cloud.
Her prayer for solace answered in God's house.

As sleep may thus be measured by its depths,
Just short of trances or of death itself–
The damsel enters a slumber few have slept.
Her spirit wrests from earth; her spirit steps.

Across a valley and its prairie floors,
Grass waves and undulates to sunbeam oars.
With each light sweep, the heather dips and soars,
Alluring souls that come from distant shores.

An ancient shepherd tends a grazing flock.
His beard is white, his hair so, every lock.
His feet, fine brass, as from a furnace brought,
His clothing glistens; sleeves and seamless frock.

She is irresistibly drawn to him,
As if led by the unseen seraphim.
This shepherd, singular, with diadem,
Has fiery eyes that pierce her soul within.

The shepherd gently calleth her by name.
"Come, Rebekah, see one sheep halted and maimed."
The shepherd showeth anger, eyes aflame;
He saith, "An enemy in darkness came!

It, helpless with disfigurement, must cope.
Its head, once high, hath now a mangled throat;
Its limbs, once able, hobbled as by rope,
Its wool, once white, hath now a scarlet coat."

"Wise shepherd, tell me, can it not be healed?
It grieveth me at what thou hast revealed;
I would, for it, my last resources yield,
To see it well, restored, back in the field.

I beg thee, let me help to mend the lamb,
To bind its broken limbs and make them sound,
Anoint its throat and keep its bandage bound.
Wash white the wool that's blood caked, matted down."

"Fair daughter, be it as thou wilt," saith he.
"Thy mercies are extended now to thee.
As thou wouldst heal the lamb, so shall thou be;
Thy limbs, thy wounds, made whole as thou shall see."

John Finds Rebekah with The Shroud of Turin

She wakens from her deep and dulcet sleep,
Still dwelling on the vision and the dream,
Having a sense of wonder, joy, and peace.
A tear emerges, courses down her cheek.

A plethora of tears fall on her flesh.
Astonishment directs her eyes to rest
On her unblemished body, healed and blessed.
This is miraculous, John shall attest,

For he has come for her, his task complete.
John, caught off-guard, is much in disbelief.
Amazement lingers, John begins to speak,
"Rebekah, God hath laid his hand on thee!

God's face commandeth clouds to disappear,
A radiance upon thee doth appear,
Some glory o'er thy shadows standeth near,
Divine favor imparted to thee here."

John, having visited in former years,
Is cognizant that relics much revered
Were housed with reverence and displayed here.
He sees them in near ruin, as he feared.

As John observes, he stares, eyes open wide,
Horror and shock manifest in his eyes.
John, pale, pulls the young woman to his side
As she becomes perplexed, much mystified.

"Look! The burial cloth of Christ our Lord.
The linen with which they had wrapped the corpse,
The shroud distinguisheth the wounds he bore."
He takes it in his arms up from the floor.

Rebekah growing faint, John braces her.
"Lord, please forgive me." She is barely heard.
"John, of its presence here, I hadst no word,
For as I slept, the shroud for cover served.

John, whilst I slept, a summon or a knell,
Whether 'twas real or dream I cannot tell,
But I wast called to the Great Shepherd's dell.
With awesome voice, He vowed to make me well."

John listens to her; he is not naïve,
Hallucinations could have come indeed,
But he cannot discount what she believes,
Nor powers of the shroud she slept beneath.

"God surely edifieth thee, daughter,
Helping thee to take away thy sorrow.
'He restoreth my soul,' saith the Psalter.
'Surely, goodness and mercy shall follow.'

Unless thou wouldst travel, make thine own way,
We must leave Salem now for our own sake.
By evening, we shouldst make camp; let's make haste.
Now let us take leave from this wretched place."

"Must we not save the Holy Shroud?" asked she.
John said, "I fear to hold such in our keep,
Else, it couldst be ruined or be taken by thieves.
To forsake it, a greater sin wouldst be."

John and Rebekah Depart Salem to a Campsite

John helped collect provisions as they left.
The ruin about them made them more bereft.
They coursed the courtyard, framing careful steps;
They gladly leave behind the scenes of death.

"Dear saint, thou art magnanimous towards me."
"Rebekah, my pleasure is to serve thee."
"But more, sir, grace and mercies do I see;
Yea, John, by heaven's kindness is thy deed.

"John said, "Truly, daughter, for thee I care,
And for thy precious life that God didst spare;
Yea, now, as for duty and thy welfare,
I shall avenge thy losses, this I swear."

By dusk, they've come some distance and are hailed
By two women camped, having bread and ale,
Who too, alone, experience travail,
They wish for pilgrim friends to be availed.

They call, "Ye good folk, art ye pilgrims too?"
John answered, "Yea, we left Salem at noon.
The city hadst no life when we withdrew."
Rebekah mourns, "Yea, we pilgrims art few."

"Rebekah suffereth deep in her heart.
Please, I am John: pray, tell us who ye art."
"She's Anne, and I'm Maria, from these parts.
This onslaught stole our loves as death doth part.

Anne's husband died last sunset in her arms,
A valiant man, he one of the gendarmes,
She'd heard of the brisk fighting and carnage,
The bells hadst brought the men out from the farms.

My man from the vineyard hadst rushed ahead,
Soon after which, they struck his throat and head.
When I came to him, he hadst ghastly bled,
And at that moment, I knew he wast dead."

Anne adds, "We didst our best to make their graves,
Whilst sorrow as a quilt wast o'er us laid.
This abhorrence hath brought disaster great,
The blood of ones we loved spilled in this place.

We bid ye, in their honor, sit and eat.
Such as we have, we'll gladly share with ye.
Have ye some ale, morsels of bread and cheese.
Our hearts need gladness now as ye canst see."

John added to the meal dried fruit, roast grain,
Rebekah, raisin cakes, from what remained.
Now, at the sight of food that was arranged,
John thanked God for it, prayed they'd be sustained.

The verdure of the forest is all about,
Its canopy, the stillness, the hooting owl,
Console them so, a quiet evening now.
Food ravenously had, enjoyed no doubt.

John shared dramatic tales brought from his past,
His father and grandfather are the cast,
Bringing mirth, which continued to the last.
Deep darkness has come, sleep approaches fast.

John said, "Our eyes art heavy, let us rest.
If ye wouldst have us by thy fire as guests."
Anne said, "May it be so at our request,
Assuaging the loneliness deep in our breast."

John props some heavy logs upon the fire,
And stirs the embers, adding sticks and briar
Until new fuel fervently catches fire,
Bids them good night, the weary folk retire.

A Wounded Man on Horseback Appears

Near dawn, John hears a horse approaching camp.
The dark morning will not reveal the mount,
Until at camp, the firelight cast around
Reveals an awesome horse in the foreground.

John has since landed squarely on his feet
With quarterstaff aloft, he poised beneath.
Deliberate eyes ablaze, fiercely keen,
Mark well, the man astride the giant steed.

The saint abruptly draws the staff away,
The rider, wounded in the battle fray
At once collapsed, the warrior slumping lay,
His life within the balance is weighed.

John leads the horse around for a better view,
The mount belonged to the palace retinue.
The hapless man, bestruck with horrid wounds
Had been searching for aid, someone he knew.

John walks the stallion up a rocky bank
And steps up higher at the horse's flank,
Faint, the man in armor clenches the mane
Until dismounted by the stalwart saint.

John hides the armor in a rocky cleft
And bears the man with care down cloven steps,
Brings him into the camp where John had slept,
And one by one, the women rise to help.

His clothing is anomalous, at first glance,
The women do not speak but look askance,
Distraught by this untoward circumstance,
Still daunted by the enemy's advance.

Below a jutting rock, a spring supplies
A source of water, which they find nearby.
They fill flagons and, to his wounds, apply
An ample bath to cleanse his neck and side.

John Goes Hunting for Deer

Except for him, they would have left that day,
Or would have searched for friends along the way.
But of concern for him, they chose to stay,
Treat his wounds, keep a vigil, and, for him, pray.

The weapons and the warhorse commandeered,
A crossbow, lance, and certain other gear
May well serve him in hunting; need grows near.
John leaves the camp in hopes of finding deer.

Birds cross the firmament with darting strokes,
A falcon sweeps the sky with broader notes
As to hide the darkness with brighter coats
Of gold and light that o'er darkness brings hope.

The forest scent adorns the early morn,
The waft of cedar in the air is borne.
John checks the wind as is the hunter's norm;
Thereby, may he not have the deer forewarned.

The horse is secured in abundant shade.
John goes on foot to the edge of a glade.
Here at an oak tree, his station is made,
Since tracks in the vicinity were laid.

It is late morning in this calm Eden.
John's watchful senses serve antecedent
To heightened awe of resplendent freedom,
Convention of nature and its ethos.

John hears thrashing; a wild boar is in view.
It must get its fill of acorns and roots.
John has no wish to make boar his pursuit,
But he would rather let the beast pass through.

The fierce boar sniffs foreign scents with its head up,
A menacing beast with razor-sharp tusks.
John knows the speed it can move through the brush.
Up into the oak tree, John catapults.

The great swine charges by as John makes way,
Its shimmering hackles divulge its rage.
Insistent that it should have John to slay,
To trample his corpse, have his flesh to flay.

The hideous boar is pacing below,
As John spies down from the oak above.
Though John is armed to take boar with the bow,
Venison, of all game, he prefers most.

John lays the crossbow crosswise at his feet,
With stock upright, held the sturdy crosspiece,
He fastens his belt around the bowstring,
Foot in the stirrup, he cocks it with a heave.

He unfastens his belt with the bow cocked,
And has a substantial quarrel in the stock.
The frenzied beast in constant motion trots.
John's aim now intermittently is blocked.

The time is now overdue for the kill.
It shall be carried out as John thus wills.
John steadily picks acorns, pockets fill,
The acorns rain down till completely spilled.

The boar stops pacing, being diverted,
It snorts, it grunts, head down, non-assertive.
John takes aim, fires the bow, unaverted,
The boar's neck is broken, and blood is spurting.

John's next move is to go back for the horse.
On return, he makes a sledge for the boar.
With broadax, he cuts staves and supports.
He guts the boar and ties it for transport.

The horse is harnessed to the makeshift sledge;
John mounts the stallion; looking back, he checks,
Then through the brush and by the tufted sedge,
He travels toward camp to the conflict's edge.

At camp, Rebekah aids the injured man,
She sees the need to do some chores at hand,
To wash his soiled garments as best she can,
And place them in the sun to have them blanched.

A gold chain within the surcoat is found
Attached to the woolen lining wound.
Astonishment grows on her face, pronounced,
Her stolen cross, linked to the chain, is found.

She placed its chain around her neck to rest.
Rebekah drew the cross close to her breast,
The cross her father gave her, she caressed,
With dreams of ever going home repressed.

A stream flows southward toward the river bend,
John halts, dismounts at the water's edge to swim,
The rippling water invigorates him.
Refreshed, he soon seeks out the drying wind.

Close range, an arrow slams into the bank.
John lunges for his bow and quiver fast–
His bow and arrow poised, his eye well trained.
Outrageous laughter breaks the silence, strained.

Out in clear view, a swarthy man appears.
John sees someone that he has known for years.
The man is grinning from ear to ear;
John fires an arrow through his hat and cheers.

"Thou foolish scoundrel!," John commenced to say,
"I might have ruined thy hat for such today,
If thou hadst merely caused me panic, nay,
But I am not inclined in such a way!"

As Hector wades toward John across the branch,
Their guffaws echo from the stony banks:
Hilarious about impulsive pranks,
And much amused that they have met by chance.

He holds the mangled hat that John defaced,
Beholding each other face to face,
They heartily slap shoulders in an embrace,
Then they discuss their meeting in this place.

Arriving at the Camp, They Meet Conflict

On John's insistence, Hector joins the ride
In John's good company to the campsite.
The men traverse the rolling countryside,
And, uneventfully, at last arrive.

They halt their horses; they look about.
John listens, hears strange voices thereabout,
Obscenities fill the air, loud and foul,
As well as the women's protests, cries, and shouts.

John digs his heels into the horse's flanks,
The equine leaps as though without restraints,
Hector follows up the lofty bank,
There they observe six men, a barbarous gang.

The women, all by force, are being held,
Their captors taunt them and amuse themselves.
John finds the armor he stashed in the cleft,
Dons what he can while Hector gives him help.

Then John unties the sledge drawn at the rear,
Steps up on stones and has the horse brought near,
Moves sturdily to mount, grasping the spear,
"Get thy bow ready, Hector, and wait here."

John rides the warhorse, makes his presence known,
Its hooves a'clatter o'er the barren stone,
Which startles all the men: surprise is shown.
He feigns to be an ally of their own.

John sits upon the stallion facing them,
The women glance at one another, then,
But keep their silence, seeing John pretend
To be in league, a comrade of these men.

One, chiding, yelps, "Ha! Vultures scour the land!
Halt, battle fiend, and cease thy war, good man!
Enjoy the spice and spoils of war at hand,
Or do ye bring more loot to us by chance?"

"Who, pray, commandeth thee?" was John's reply,
"As seeing thine escutcheons art laid by."
"I, Bomar, give the orders, even I,
And on Prince Rabac's orders, wouldst I die!

I go to battle for Akaan, the King."
Bomar continued, "By his seal and ring
Gold is assured, and my success shall bring
Fine commendations and enriching things.

Didst I not capture Krislos, Salem's King,
Who came ashore from a shipwreck, stumbling he?
He proudly wore a crown–a seaweed wreath!
The gods dispatched his troops in the open sea.

I have laid Salem waste and join the rest.
Detachments raid the land at my behest,
As thou dost under Necor and his crest.
Five Princes range the land for full conquest,

As, incidentally, didst this dying man
Serve under Necor, having a command.
He, by his wounds, now bleedeth on this land,
Contemptuous to stain it if he can.

This man is Elaam, o'er whom hangs death's spell,
A man of rank on whom an ill fate fell.
He hath a knife to end his own life well,
Not die in shame by hands of infidels."

John said, "Let such foes stain this land at last.
Let birds of prey be gorged when they've amassed.
The vulture circleth on the current mass;
It doth portend what cometh soon to pass."

One of them yells, "Thou art a morbid ghoul!
Ill dreams stalk thee as jackals track their food."
Rau said, "See not, he warreth with us, fool?
His armor serveth as a specious tool!"

John roars, "This maiden ye didst vilely rape!
Her relatives, ye slaughtered, none escaped.
God's sanctuary, ye didst desecrate;
As Salem's holy saints in blood wert draped."

Bomar cries, "Such shall be the end ye'll meet!"
Rau followed, "Thou art food for dogs to eat.
Thy rotting bones shall lie among the weeds,
And these trulls shall accompany thee!"

John yells, "I shall avenge them in this hour
For what ye didst to them under thy pow'r!
Cowards! Ye make the defenseless cower,
Thy gory heads shall burst to feed the flow'r!"

The snorting charger paws the quaking ground
Most dreadful, as the thund'rous hooves resound,
The eyes, with scorching fury, spy around,
Ignite raw nerve and sinew to confound.

Hector is eyeing closely every move,
Assessing each target, which first to choose.
With his longbow aimed and poised, an arrow flew,
Felling a spearman, he then reloads to shoot.

John must be swift to execute the raid,
Advance on them while they are disarrayed,
Deny them weapons use, or use delayed,
He profits from his clever masquerade,

John spurs the flanks, unleashing potent force,
As though of centaur flesh, the man, the horse,
Incredulous with power set the course,
To slay as fiery vengeance runs its course.

The horse, valiant in its marauding state,
Shows brilliance in what all John undertakes.
The master's tactics, it must not mistake,
Must leave utter destruction in its wake.

Full pelt, John encircles his rivals there,
As if to draw them under net or snare.
A theater of wrath and deadly dare,
He strikes down two with none in mind to spare.

Anne and Maria manage to run free.
Rebekah finds refuge behind a tree
To avoid being trampled by the steed
Or be struck as the riposte is increased.

Bomar and Rau are now mounting their steeds.
Maneuvers done, instinctive, with good speed,
Armed well enough, expecting to succeed.
In a quick dispatch of John, a vengeful deed.

For hand-to-hand combat, Hector attacks,
Armed with sword and dagger, approaching fast
He drags down one who's mounting on horseback
The clash, flash of the blade, a final slash.

The officer is grossly disemboweled,
The sight and stench fit for carrion fowl.
He grimaces. Once boastful, profane, proud,
The enemy's insolent visage cowed.

Bomar attempts escape from the attack.
John challenges Bomar to bring him back,
To joust, or as it were, to force contact.
His opponent halts; Bomar's stallion tacks.

"Bomar, put on thy full suit of armor!
Choose thy weapon, as well as thy charger.
Cloaks of violence clothe thee no longer,
For thy life shall be stripped like a garment!"

John's face set, his stare frozen toward Bomar,
Eyes cold as stone seem to focus afar.
The stallion, poised, waits to make the bold charge,
John lowers his lance, it fixed on the mark.

Bomar's face twitches, maintaining a smirk.
John's mighty stallion, reeling to the spur,
The rapturous thunder of hooves is heard,
Peripheral scenes pass by in a blur.

Each man has his eyes driven in his foe,
Where the lance's tip should follow with woe,
And its bescorching shaft would drive it home,
And the terrible wrath of it be known.

The rush is entrancing as the blitz unwinds,
The riders seem caught in suspended time,
Entrapped in this tale, horrible, resigned,
Where life and death commingle, intertwined.

The horses, near collision, boldly advance,
The stout horsemen brace, steadying the lance.
Opponents strike, Bomar is growing blanched,
He, struck, fell from his horse, lance in his hand.

John sees Bomar's frothy blood gushing forth.
But John does not rejoice; this is no sport,
Nor is there pleasure felt in keeping scores.
This fight is just, and John feels no remorse.

Rebekah is Abducted

Rau seizes the moment during the fight
To take Rebekah and fast leave the site,
For it is dusk, and now, by mask of night
He may succeed if the scant tracks aren't spied.

Rebekah and Elaam, Rau suspects now,
Are collaborators, and the scrolls found,
Indicate that they are mutually bound,
With Elaam near death, she's valued by Rau.

Rebekah has wrapped the shroud about her,
It must be kept with her to be preserved,
To her consternation, the shroud disturbs,
As visions inadvertently occur.

When Rebekah can't be found, John is told,
Nor can they account for Rau or his role,
But that Rau has kidnapped her is supposed.
John must pursue her–but should he now go?

Lest Rau summon soldiers to strike while dark,
John decides that he should stay and stand guard.
"Roast the boar," he said, "or we shall all starve,"
John asks Hector to speak with him apart.

"I must find Rebekah soon tomorrow,"
John said, "These in camp shall meet more sorrow,
At Prince Rabac's right hand, they shall be martyrs.
Thou alone must save them from the horror.

My vow to fight must be solemnly kept,
For her and our king, war unto the death,
My duty fulfilled to these and the rest,
And save the shroud she doth hold near her breast.

Krislos' army from foreign wars shall come,
Leaderless, for Krislos elsewhere hath gone.
We must yet learn where he abideth long,
For his country doth need its Leader home.

If thou wouldst save thyself and these rescue,
Gather what thou canst and prepare to move.
Take horses. As for Elaam, save him too
That we may learn of Akaan and his troops."

Valiantly, John has destroyed the last man.
John and Hector look around where they stand,
At rich food, gold, and jewels there at hand,
Fine weaponry and horses in the camp.

John kneels next to Elaam and has him drink,
As well, John gives him broth and bread to eat,
Holds the cross of St. Laud, prays in belief
That God will heal the wounds that run so deep.

As they ate, John began speaking to them
About saving Rebekah, his attempt,
But they must leave with Hector, follow him
Across the river to a remote realm.

John gathers provisions for the long term,
For he knows not the day of his return.
He must go rest, but tell them farewell first,
By early light, he'll start the hard sojourn.

Rau leads, and six horsemen follow after,
Their destination is Akaan's palace.
Rebekah is now equipped for travel,
Allowed to have her own horse and saddle.

Rau will no more permit her to be harmed,
For she may have to stand before Akaan
To tell him about the scrolls, as forewarned,
Since Elaam was brought down by the gendarme.

Rebekah has regained her composure,
A near sense of calm around the soldiers,
More freedom, and when speaking, much bolder,
She, within days, is seen as much older.

She is tense and concerned over the scrolls
Or about what they think she can disclose,
One's life can hinge on what a person knows,
Or lost as well by what may be supposed.

John shall use weapons, clothes, armor, and crest,
Enemies shall be forthrightly addressed,
That John's need for information be met,
An imposter's free passage, it suggests.

John's friends are encouraged by the fifth day,
Surprisingly, Elaam's fever abates,
No new bouts with delirium displayed,
At last, the strange look in his eyes has waned.

John's Trail Through the Forest

John is forging ahead to the northeast,
The main route of Akaan's troops will he seek.
Having lost Rau's trail, the prospect seems bleak
Of finding her soon, as he had first believed.

A gust of wind, abrupt and compelling
Rattles the still forest, sticks, leaves pelting,
Dark clouds tumultuous and large swelling,
Glower from their habitat and setting.

All told, then, John has quite sufficient awe.
At a riverbank, he decides to cross
To find cover before the heavens fall,
While shallow water threatens not at all.

He rides from the river to higher ground.
Bold, towering cliffs, statuesque surround
A yawning dark cave in one recess found
Bids John and the horse to the sculpted sound.

John watches lights in the sky, bright bolts fork,
Arcs of white against black menacing forms.
He gets wood to the cave before the storm
And finds sufficient forage for the horse.

As the majestic horse feeds on stubble,
John strokes the horse over the soft muzzle
And along the steed's massive neck muscle;
A horse, which with great fury, meets trouble.

John shall name the white charger Bolt O'Wrath.
In the distance, as far as a stone is cast,
He sees a she-wolf with two whelps, both black,
Darting fast after her quickening tracks.

With one great descending lightning bolt
Comes forth a shattering, earth-splitting jolt,
Confounding every eye, every ear takes note,
With every cleft and grotto there exposed.

Momentary dots, yellow and purple,
Orbit in John's eyes and seem eternal.
The stunned pups, reoriented, erstwhile,
Wander about the she-wolf in circles.

Inaudible to John, they seem to cry,
Minute by minute, he observes the site,
Discomfited pups cuddle at her side,
Alas, John thinks that the she-wolf has died.

John walks into the smoldering milieu,
He crouches at the malaise he views,
Patiently coaxing the pups from their mew,
Until, inch by inch, they both toward him move.

John extends to them pieces of dried meat,
Which one small whelp takes quickly, then retreats.
The other remains, licks John's hand and eats,
Yards away, torrents of rain come in sheets.

John grabs the whelps, each arm a pup beneath,
The furious heavens give full release,
Of boisterous winds that chase, like a leaf,
These to the cave in near flight with winged speed.

Who arrive variously found, unfurled,
Animated by their surreal whirl.
The cave welcomes them, a motionless world,
Excepting the projectiles the wind hurls.

Daylight ebbs; John proceeds to build a fire.
Tedious details in darkness conspire
To prolong his achievement and desire,
His satisfaction from a blazing pyre.

Nonetheless, he ignites the last tinder,
Then, small sticks with scintillating vigor
Impose upon the wood until rendered
In flames, fallen logs, the eye of splendor.

The pups conceivably would clash with man,
Wildish, but never purely wild again.
Wild pits itself against rule or command,
Which shall rule, be ruled, at the other's hand?

To rule over the earth is man's instinct,
For God charged, 'subdue the earth,' the edict,
Soul under God, which makes mankind distinct,
Man's rationale to rule over all things.

The source of all civility and peace
Shall rule. The wild and lawless one shall cease,
Devourers, none to ravage the meek,
The lion shall lie down beside the sheep.

But the pups have the instinct of the pup,
Unlike the she-wolf, wise, wary adult,
Her instinct not, by man, yet corrupt,
Would not be ruled, nor her freedom given up.

Bolt O'Wrath looks down at the little wolves,
The two huff and growl at the stallion's hooves,
John notes their supple coats, the sheen-like wool,
Both pups, green-eyed, with fur as black as soot.

The spry pups roll and scuffle in the cave,
John looks on, amusement shows on his face.
As he eats, they run to him for a taste,
"What shall become of them?" he contemplates.

The lordly wind and tempestuous rites
Of angry Nature with flamboyant might
Speak to all dominions to vilify,
While God of heaven speaks in the still of night.

To the Creator, John bows in homage
And gratitude for the unique lodging,
For the horse and provisions, a godsend,
This odyssey forged by God's providence.

John's Dream in the Cave

As nightfall fills its boundaries with shade,
Inviting fitful phantoms to its place,
Taking man's sleeping soul in its embrace,
John falls into deep slumber in the cave.

He dreams within a dream that ghosts convene,
The enemies he slew appear, chiding.
John shivers, asks the reason that they meet.
"We came to heap our curses upon thee!

Why hast thou sent us here to such a place?
On earth, sufferings pale, art a foretaste,
Such is it, they compare not, none equate.
This bale is completely barren of grace.

There is no place named likened unto Hell,
Horrible pain and suffering e'er felt,
Forever, yea, in that word it doth tell.
Deliver us from here, give us thy help!

Tell God, vengeful slayer, of thine own guilt,
That we shouldst be free, for our blood wast spilt.
For it wast thou who came of thine own will,
With rage in thy heart with an eye to kill."

John said, "Ye eagerly charge me with fault,
For saving the women under assault!
Would ye have released them simply with talk?
Nay, blood was a prerequisite in thy thought.

The likes of ye do make it Hell on earth,
Liars, deceivers, destroyers, perverse.
Ye ruled the world, but Hell is the converse,
Now ye art as bereft of pow'r as mirth.

Evil men know heaven is not their fate,
Unless they are deluded in their faith.
Such men care not for truth before the grave,
They love their sin, the truth they will not face.

From creation, God gave men a conscience,
After which God sent the holy prophets,
Crying, 'Repent!' But their hearers mocked them,
Then spake through his Son, the very Godhead.

Thus, I cannot deliver ye from Hell,
For I didst not e'er send ye there to dwell,
Ye heeded not God, but to truth were deaf.
If ye hadst heeded heav'n, all wouldst be well."

The enemies left, sorrowfully so,
To their torment, for there was no more hope;
Cursing John, railing at him, so they spoke.
Hearing their words, John, perspiring, awoke.

THE GATE
AT HASLIM'S
CASTLE

John's Travel Resumes

The morning sun splits the reluctant sky,
Exposing forest wounds and myriad cries.
The wood, by its resolve and silent pride,
Hushes complaining voices far and wide.

John has let the stallion graze and drink,
Saddles Bolt O'Wrath and draws up the cinch,
Saddle bags are repacked and strapped to rings;
He checks and reexamines everything.

John mounts the horse, sees the whelps on the ground,
They look up and anxiously run around.
John rides away; the pups, too, are trail-bound.
John patiently halts the steed, then dismounts.

He must test if they would go or reside,
Nor would he leave them there helpless besides.
But how to care for them—he must decide,
John stoops, lifting the wolves up at his sides.

The saddlebags he shall try– he's hard-pressed.
John's need is to press urgently ahead,
He allows time to pay a lesser debt,
A decision he hopes he won't regret.

John tackles the journey with its rigors,
With frequent backtracking to make it north,
Through mountainous climbs with cold streams to ford,
He travels, determined to stay the course.

Exploring, John rides through a narrow pass.
He is rewarded by a great contrast,
As foliage gives way, a valley unmasked
Looms before him, unending, lush, and vast.

Haslim, the old Duke, has his horse saddled,
On the Duke's right arm rests his trained falcon.
He shall be gone the day from the castle,
Hunt small game in the cool forest, dabble.

The Duke finds a solitary arbor.
The swift bird snares game close by, some farther,
Striking with the art of a fine archer,
Haslim, thrilled, watches it reach the target.

John hears someone yelling from a thicket.
The Duke is swearing, all the while limping.
His horse gallops away, having kicked him.
The Duke's arm still braced, the bird revisits.

The Duke hobbles about in pain with cramps.
John rides into the thicket and dismounts
With concern to see what it's all about,
But to see Haslim motion, point, and shout.

The Duke's leg, swelling, quite large it has become,
John assists him to a fallen tree trunk,
Haslim complains that his leg is now numb,
John cuts the tight stocking away at once.

John said, "My name is Ekraam from Necor.
He hath sent me expeditiously forth,
To bring a good accounting and report,
To the palace of King Akaan's court."

John found the mare and assisted Haslim,
Bringing Haslim to his waiting castle.
They halt their horses at the iron stanchion.
The Duke signaled the guards in the bastion.

The guards give word to have the gate opened,
John and the Duke cross the bridge and the moat,
Causing considerable commotion,
His subjects fear the Duke's leg is broken.

Now arrive the physician and the priest
With guards flanking them; the Duke is tired and weak.
"If on behalf of thy lord I may speak,"
Said John, "He wast kicked hard by his own steed."

The head guard spoke, "Good, if thy words be true,
But woe to thee if thou hast harmed the Duke!"
The old Duke silenced him with a rebuke.
"Quiet! The man's goodwill toward us is proved.

Wouldst he bring me here if he'd caused me harm?
By chance heardeth me, sensing my alarm,
He turned aside, and he my life didst guard,
This is Necor's officer named Ekraam."

Haslim's left leg, where the hoof made contact,
The Physician believes the bone is cracked,
The glancing blow left the bone intact.
Haslim should do well and recover fast.

A curious boy, looking at John's horse,
Observes the little pups' complaints and noise,
Sees the bags on the saddle, and spots the source.
John pays the lad to feed and keep them warm.

John's alias, Ekraam, must serve for now
Until the moment Rebekah is found.
To have John's name known must not be allowed
Lest his scheme be intercepted by Rau.

Hospitality at the Castle

The next day, they're served an elegant meal.
The Duke's officials, hearing the bells peal,
Gather in the castle's great hall of shields,
Symbol and vestige of their Commonweal.

John has been given a place at the table,
Immaculate preparation savored
By nobility and those so favored,
To eat with the Duke's elite and faithful.

The priest offers a prayer of gratitude
For the exquisite offering of food,
Servings of meat, fish, tortes, and luscious fruits,
With the best of wine and fine spirits brewed.

Haslim, helped to the table, was seated,
Wishing to converse with guests while eating,
States an enigma with which he's dealing.
Christ's words he's quoting, 'Love thine enemies.'

Haslim asks, "If ye be out with thy troops,
Fighting foes, is thy sword refrained from use?
And by night, wouldst ye feed foes, all induced
To eat well, nourishing them with good food?

Wherein is the supposition of love,
If, by day, a man thirsts for the foe's blood?
Or yet, say, with a presumed hate or grudge,
Favors going out and warring with such?

Doth, 'Love thy foe' mean to let him strike first?
Nay, nor doth love give drink to quench his thirst,
Lest refreshed, he fights thee for all he's worth
And behead thee, which one shouldst well deserve."

A noble spoke, "In the foe put no trust,
If thou art under commandment to love,
First, defeat the enemy, as thou must,
Disarm him, then get guidance from above.

To otherwise think is to love fables,
For to 'love' thine enemy is fatal.
What virtue in the foe's behavior
Maketh him worthy of care or favor?"

Another noble contributes as well,
"In heaven's womb, love doth presume to dwell.
Love hath no certain place in war, I tell,
For there is a contradiction, war is hell!

Famine and fire, and deadly pestilence,"
He continues, "Art these not war's essence?
And these war's consequences, war's weapons?
And mourners, cripples, thieves, the evidence?"

Several nobles are heard affirming him.
They look at one another, and Haslim
As if to reinforce the last comment.
Haslim pauses and thoughtfully strokes his chin.

A comment then is uttered by the Priest.
"Good doctrine yet is lacking as ye speak.
Of all God's laws, love is greatest, not least.
It is to the spirit ye shouldst give heed.

Thy theology is somewhat at fault.
In reason, humans do err by default,
Creating parameters for God's law,
Which doth misappropriate what Christ taught.

Christ is the Prince of Peace, not the Prince of War.
Let not love be conjoined to myths in war.
Love reconcileth, war doth part by the sword.
War destroyeth, but love doth build and restore.

God maketh worlds, God establisheth them,
He defineth kingdoms, domains, and realms,
Sovereign o'er all flesh, God knoweth all ends.
God enableth peace and loveth all men."

He continues, "The first war wast in heaven.
When Satan chose to war in his rebellion,
God cast him down to earth from His presence,
War yet rageth from Satan's aggression!

Therefore, we still have war in this dark world,
Until Christ shall return with wrath in store,
To conquer and to reign forevermore,
Then nations shall not learn war anymore."

A young official next ventures a word
Desiring somewhat to impress, be heard,
Feels safe in quoting from Solomon's works,
Espousing wisdom as the Priest might urge.

"There is a time for war, a time for peace,
A time to love, to hate, to laugh, to weep,
A time to cast away, a time to keep;
There is a time to lose, a time to seek." (Eccles. 3:8)

Ekraam says, "Although we be not prescient,
As such, man must make the most of reason
And the most of love, acting with credence.
As for war, as said, war hath its season.

Pure wrath, pure love, that only God can'st show.
But man, the face and soul of war doth know.
Pure innocence, pure guilt, none wouldst suppose.
Let justice rule first in the hour of woe.

Rather, let war be judged by love instead.
Shall the sword, then, liberate or oppress?
Shall the sword protect life and counter threats,
Or be used for heedless slaughter and death?

Who but man doth choose between peace and war?
Let him end evil before he endeth war!
War doth start war, but war must end war.
The wise and just know when to bear the sword."

Haslim speaks, "Thou dost dress as a true foe.
The fabric of thy heart is not made so!
Pray, weapons call thee 'master,' so to own.
Mayest thou in battle thine passions hold."

Haslim's Request of John

Haslim continues, "Akaan hath me taxed
Of mine gold, livestock, wool, and grain, he asks.
But mine greatest treasure, King Akaan hath."
Haslim's head drops low; his eyes are downcast.

With trembling voice he says, "It's the Duchess,
Held hostage, my short life Akaan crusheth.
I fear she doth languish in the dungeon.
Akaan wouldst guarantee his own success.

My castle is for his strategic use.
To have me manage all the land's produce,
Maintain its stores to feed his passing troops,
And for Akaan to get his levied dues.

If thou art going to him, I beg thee,
Return to my castle and bring it to me
Word of my lovely Duchess, how she be,
If she desireth heaven, death doth seem sweet.

Give her a letter from me, I beseech.
I will pay gold what thou dost ask of me
Only regarding my request, concede
To show grace in this matter," Haslim pleads.

Ekraam is pretending to be unmoved,
A stoic expression he has assumed,
Though a tear pressing threatens to exude,
Ekraam's resolve has his feelings subdued.

Ekraam said, "Haslim, thou art most cunning.
As the hawk that circleth whilst hunting,
Thou dost encircle before confronting,
Determined as thou art in triumphing.

If I deny thy plea, which thou hast voiced,
I must eat my words, love I have endorsed.
As the hawk preys, thou with snares art adroit,
My weakness thou dost eagerly exploit.

But then, thy gold offered shall serve me well,
Exploitation, likewise, bringeth wealth.
Warriors seize its ruthless route, though through hell-
For moments of glory, opulent pelf."

Haslim says, "The 'eye' of conscience torments,
As a 'warden' of the soul seeth men,
Fully assaying how their lives art spent,
Whether warriors exploit or defend."

Ekraam asks, "Dost thou know one such as this?
Hath one, named Rau, at this place made a visit,
Or passed he near here? For our paths have missed.
Tell me if some good word of him exists."

"To answer," said Haslim, "Rau rode this way,
He and six horsemen with a comely maid,
Headed for Pross, he hadst not much to say,
Nor for persons expected didst he wait."

Ekraam replied, "Then prepare thy letter.
Soon, I shall leave–the sooner, the better.
Delay not, or thou shall be a debtor,
As my price shall render thee a beggar."

Diligently, the anxious odyssey
Is spun to find one lost, a darling sheep,
Ere to rescue her from the lion's teeth,
Steal the prey from ungodly beasts.

Or else ennoble her dishonored blood,
Jaws forced, release, extinguished life give up,
And as the sheep's ear or remaining tuft
Is snatched away, hate does homage to love.

To find Rebekah before they reach Pross
Is the awful dilemma faced by John,
To fail shall find her placed in prison bonds.
She shall be at the mercy of Akaan.

For twenty days more to travel northeast,
More nights and days shall yield their cold and heat
His brow shall sweat, the cold shall chill his feet,
His zealous eye shall signal him from sleep.

John sights a campfire on the sixth evening,
Aggressive forces surge in his being,
Caution secondary in his thinking,
He gallops toward the presumed enemy.

But imagined foes vanish, dance away,
One with servants beside the fire lay.
There is quiet, and the man rises dismayed,
As John comes near, the man hails with his hand raised.

The tent possesses generous floor space,
Hides and rugs from the Orient, ornate,
Line the tent's womb, such on the floor is laid.
Balfour has stocked many items to trade.

Effulgent air, aromatic with spice
Of Balfour's trade, his savored merchandise
Brings with it its particular delights,
Ambiance is least expected at this time.

An oil lamp burns with a hospitable glow,
Renders its own welcome, warm and yellow,
Changes day's starkness to evening mellow,
Casts convivial cheer o'er the shadows.

Balfour took from the fire a pot of tea
That they might enjoy the brew and its heat.
They retrieved hot stones when the fire had ceased,
Wrapped the campfire stones for warmth at their feet.

The men settle in the tent for the night,
Conversing by the flickering lamplight,
With good shelter from the brisk winds outside,
John welcomes this good moment and respite.

John asks, "Hast thou seen King's men pass hither,
Horsemen led by Rau with a prisoner?"
Wryly answered, "Seven men wert with her,
A king's ransom paid for her, I figure."

The merchant and John exchange the latest news.
Balfour has learned much along this trade route.
The well-traveled man knows Haslim the Duke,
Of Krislos' capture and imminent doom.

John mulls over these things Balfour reports,
Says, "The trip ahead awaiteth me, north.
I will get some provisions from thy stores."
"Why not ride with my traders?" asks Balfour.

John and Traders Head Toward Pross
Creaks and clamor, five wagons' wagging tongues
Complain against the drays' tortuous tugs,
The drays balk, but to trader's lash succumb,
Men toiling to enlarge the bulk of their funds.

The fields of fortune, traders yearn to reap.
The sun exhales hot breath, its scorching heat,
Thick thirst and moiling conspire to foil their strength.
The men and horses strive, freight unrelieved.

A caravan route intersects toward Pross,
Where an outpost stands, a place to lodge.
The weary traders are ready to stop,
Shelter there, and devour meals served from pots.

Arabesque carpets, Ghazi spreads around,
Removes his cloak, reclines thereon to lounge,
Loosely, a gold chain 'round his neck swings out,
He palms promptly to house it in a pouch.

"Aye, of Akaan, I caution of his greed,
Avariciously taketh what doth please.
His eyes art heir of what they, wanton, see,
Bulging moneybags art his right to seize."

John, nodding, thanks him. Akmed leans forward,
Nibbling on terfa, voice somewhat lowered,
"Levies on our goods Akaan endorseth.
The Emir is Akaan's chief enforcer."

"Emir!" John interrupts, probing Akmed.
"'Twas told, Emir Elaam died," Akmed said,
"Peasants beheld him wounded, they alleged,
For reward, didst take him to Pross, near death.

Prior to this, he'd served the King in war.
Akaan holdeth Elaam in high regard,
Preemptively placed peasants under guard,
But Elaam didst hire them as servants in his charge.

Emir Elaam suffereth yet from wounds,
But is not slack exacting revenues.
Tax officers collect surtaxes due.
Elaam is strict, record keeping showeth proof."

John and Traders Aid an Injured Monk

As their travel advances the next day,
The traders maintain their efficient pace,
Though John desires haste for Rebekah's sake,
Alas, John's journeys never lack delays.

John's horse is spurred, the gait briskly advanced.
Not far ahead, he sees an injured man,
A monk there, in distress, attempts to stand,
For thieves had struck, stalking a caravan.

The monk groans, "I wast robbed by two horsemen!"
Pointing where they went with much exertion,
Ghazi and John join in pursuit of them,
Akmed remains assisting the victim.

The errant thieves brandish their swords in haste,
John wields a cudgel, unhorses one knave,
While Ghazi, a well-trained swordsman, sword in play,
Subdues the other rogue under his sway.

The thief, which Ghazi rived with his curved sword,
Dreadfully bleeds and, for his life, implores.
The thief John struck careened from off his horse,
One arm is dislocated by the force.

In the aftermath of the encounter,
Akmed arrives with James; they're dismounting.
The disabled bandits are surrounded,
Fearing death, "Have mercy!" they are shouting.

The monk's leg is made stable with a splint.
John sees dark bruises inflicted on him,
For James had been beaten by the bandits.
James moans, barely speaking, "I forgive them."

John's fury escalates, highly incensed,
He reels around, he sees the bandits cringe,
Their faces white with fear; John glares at them.
"No! No!" the monk cries, "No more blood, my friend."

The monk's hands raised, he gestures to John; he pleads,
"To God belongeth vengeance for the thieves,
God forbid! Pray, don't hate thine enemies,
Assist them, bind up their injuries."

John retrieves all that from James was stolen,
Akmed rounds up the thieves' cache and horses,
Quips, "Payback for James' loss, a mere token."
James' voice fails him, protests unspoken.

Akmed unties his horse and quickly mounts,
Ghazi tells John, "Water nearby wast found,
He left to give orders to make camp,
Seems better that monk James not be moved now."

"Indeed, that wouldst be best for him," said John.
Ghazi adds, "Herbs and ointments, we have all,
Which shouldst help relieve James' pain and trauma."
Akmed brings John his weapons and armor.

He nettles John with a good-natured tease,
"A man ought not be without weaponry,
Seeing how thy day didst fare, mightst have need."
John gifted Akmed a dagger and sheath.

"Ziba ahead," says Ghazi, "We have a trade.
Tomorrow, these two thieves wilt be arraigned,
They both shall stand before the magistrate."
"Farewell," said John, "With thine aid, James wast saved."

The Monks' Concern for James

Monks at the monastery are astir,
Their brother, Frater James, has not returned.
The Abbot bids five monks, "Act on concerns,"
They leave the abbey to commence a search.

Regretting they had let James go alone,
Worries among them on their faces are shown.
O'er each breath, prayers rush, o'er each step, each road.
What darkness would forbid, torches disclose.

The monks' habits are pronounced by their lamps.
John sees them, welcomes all of them to camp,
Says, "Frater James suffers, his wounds I've bound."
They rush to their brother and gather around.

James Returns to the Abbey

Assuredly, a monk hears cartwheels turn,
Anticipating Frater James' return,
Suspecting James was harmed, he's much concerned.
At once he leaves his chore: the butterchurn.

"James is enroute," Abbot Ambrose is told,
Ambrose looks on, sight grievous to behold,
A soldier, with James, makes his blood run cold,
Scenarios imagined, manifold.

The monastery doorman, there of late,
Stands. Monks rush past him, nor do hesitate.
With apprehension great, they swing the gate,
The monks stop short, heedful of James' grave state.

James awakens with eyes opened widest,
Aware, he weeps. Monks give him help, their best.
Respectfully, John waits for all the rest.
With heads inclined, monks welcome John, their guest.

Ambrose follows promptly, now arriving,
Comes forward with humility, smiling,
Blesses James, while to John, Scripture citing,
"I wast a stranger, and ye took me in." (Matt 25:35)

John acknowledges the Abbot's greeting.
"Thy kind welcome is gratefully received.
Thy brother, Frater James, wast harmed by thieves,
My duty wast to save him, as thou seest."

John and the Abbot Converse

"I'm John, a pilgrim, who at Salem wast,
I seek a pilgrim held captive at Pross.
Akaan hath humbled Salem by assault,
Death and destruction on it he hath wrought.

I lament, as once didst Jeremiah;
"How lonely is 'Salem,' the city sigheth,
None comfort her, to a widow likened,
Her gates desolate, in ruin lieth."

Ambrose says, "I grieve for Salem as well."
John adds, "Pross doth abhor the infidel.
Pray for my quest to follow, I'm compelled.
Pray for our anguished King who's heard Death's knell,"

Ambrose, with misgivings, "What is thy plan?
To ride a warhorse, as if by command,
Accoutrement, armor, weapons? Thou shan't!
Pray leave these here till they're required at hand.

First go to Pross, whilst there, a plan conceive.
Then, learn how to cautiously proceed.
A horse thou shall have, to that I shall see."
"Thy plan, Abbot, bringeth me much relief."

John speaks as they stroll through the abbey hall,
"I wilt show thee the warhorse in the stall
Named Bolt O'Wrath and why he is so called;
The battle scent rouseth snorting and pawing."

When John and Ambrose reach the horses' shed,
Grand Bolt O' Wrath pitches his noble head.
His strong, arched neck flings his white mane outspread,
His whiny resonates in complement.

Deacon Andrew is summoned from the nave,
Called on to help John get underway.
Beholding Bolt O'Wrath, he is amazed,
Exulting, "Glory! Look what God hath made."

"The horse stayeth here, "John said, "as advised,
Except my armor shall stay by my side,
Concealed. I'll pose as a trader for the time.
Two horses I'll need, one for merchandise."

His saddlebags are hanging in the stall.
John unbuckles one bag pegged on the wall,
From a pouch, some gold coins he withdraws,
Hands them to Ambrose. He refuses all.

"Kindly, thou hast brought James to recover.
Always, thou art welcome as a brother.
All thy needs, thou shall have for thy journey.
Freely ride one horse and pack the other."

THE GATE

OF PROSS

SURVEILLED

John Arrives at Pross

At Pross, the market sector overwhelms,
The merchant's wares are displayed everywhere.
Tents line the streets, all kinds of goods to sell,
Camels in holds around the city are kept.

John comes to a halt where traders talk and eat,
Greets them when he dismounts; some nod, some speak.
He asks, "Where's a corral to keep my steeds?"
One points, "A goodly one is down the street."

John goes, taking the cue, as directed.
At the stable he waits, horses tethered.
John thinks he's hearing muffled expletives,
He's flabbergasted when out walks Hector.

Quite boisterous laughter bursts out when they meet,
Hysterically, a serendipity,
Until their mirth subsides, they cannot speak.
The hubbub nearby drowns their raucous glee.

Says Hector, "Bring the horses to the stall,
They wilt be kept, and what thou hast withal.
I keep Elaam's steeds for his beck and call.
We servants he didst hire when he wast brought."

John at Hector's Hut

That he's in safe shelter, John's in good cheer.
"As thou hast guessed, I've tracked Rebekah here,
To rescue her if there is some way clear.
I have no means except by the Emir.

If anyone knoweth a way, in truth,
It wouldst be thou. This so, we must collude.
I couldst save her, but of course, hang thou wouldst,"
Hector shouts, "Get thee out, thou bumbling fool!"

John laughs quite heartily as Hector glares.
"Thou wilt escape the gallows," John declares.
"Show me where Elaam serves, thou shall be spared.
I'll not need thy help further to prepare."

Hector said, "Tomorrow, third hour of the day,
Emir Elaam's horse to him I wilt take.
Observe, as I do so, where he doth stay,
Then carry out thy plan without my aid.

"Dear friend," Hector pleads, "Here do spend the night.
Do, in an unclean stall, lovely alight."
Rollicking wit, Hector fails not to cite.
John says, "Friendship's aroma, essence thine."

Unfolding is the scene that Hector planned,
The exchequer's door opens; Elaam stands,
The horse's reins are placed in Elaam's hands.
Now, has the stratagem of John advanced.

John's Strategy at Pross

For John, reality thereafter strikes,
Miscalculation could cost friends their lives.
Action must not be a roll of the dice,
But occasioned, optimal, timely, right.

To meet Elaam, a means must be devised,
A door of opportunity espied,
A course of action now must be outlined.
He will consult with Hector for apt times.

Hector decides to aid John; he is key.
"Hand off a note to Elaam with the steed:
    'John, from Salem, wants urgently to meet.
    Of utmost importance that he see thee!'

Elaam is unexpectedly forthwith.
In just three days, Elaam will meet with him.
That day, at the ninth hour, a hearing he will give,
Granting John's spirit a much-needed lift.

John wears a new tunic and cloak to meet
At Elaam's quarters near the mezzanine,
With armor bundled to support his scheme,
When, at the stair landing, guards intervene.

"Halt!" swords drawn, "Who art thou? Go no farther!"
"I'm a friend, bringing the Emir's armor."
"How didst thou obtain the Emir's armor?"
"He came to camp, near death, on his charger."

At that time, Elaam, hearing commotion,
Calls out to them, "What this man saith is so,
Allow him to enter, now ye may go!"
To John, Elaam relates, "Thy voice I know."

"Aye, I am John, as thou hast ascertained."
"And thou," the Emir said, "hied from Salem
To bring my armor?" John said, "As thou sayest,
And talk with thee in private, if I mayst."

"Speak on," Elaam, patient to hear John out.
"Rebekah, by force, wast taken by Rau,
I want thee to release her now."
Elaam huffs, "Thou knowest I've no such pow'r,

That King Akaan hath her as his mistress!"
"Sir, thou rescued her once." John persisted.
"But incumbent now!?" Elaam resisted.
John said, "I risk my life implicitly."

Elaam, becoming tense, "Rescue her how?"
His mind flashed to that dark night and hour,
When for Rebekah, he gambled with Rau;
His sense of probity overwhelms him now.

Growing quiet, Elaam is now seated.
"Knavish Rau wouldst have this chair," said Elaam.
"To replace me he seeketh a reason,
Such as the accusation of treason.

What is blocking Rau now is but one thing,
That is Akaan's trust in my loyalty.
The armor from Salem thou didst bring me,
Rau shall report in the hearing of the King.

Krislos doth face the gallows in three months
At Gargoyle, rites of burial and 'plot.'
Rebekah there, actions? Who knoweth what?
Keep thou the armor, now take leave of Pross!"

As was predicted, Rau speaks to Akaan,
Suspecting that the visitor is John,
Who came bringing Elaam's armor and arms,
Implicating Elaam, "Be duly warned."

"This John," Akaan retorts, "Guards unmasked him,
Veiled, this Salemite devil assassin,
Twice, hath sought the Emir's life, attacked him.
To conspire against me, Elaam hasn't."

John Warned Returns to the Monastery

Straightway, John goes to the corral sector.
Circumstances he'll relate to Hector,
Seeking his assessment and perspective,
John's appearance–ill-timed, unexpected.

With a harried expression on John's face,
Hector, concerned, hands o'er chores to his aide,
Motions for John to come over his way,
To hear from John what Elaam had to say.

Summarily, John tells him what took place.
Afraid of being caught, John must escape
To the Abbey. John tells Hector the way,
Must let John know the execution date.

Hector leads, a prime Arabian steed,
He does not underestimate the need.
If John is not soon gone, soon he shall be.
John's nemesis would slay him were he seized.

Hector makes equipage for John's armor,
Lashed behind the saddle of the charger.
Hastily, John mounts for his departure,
Man and horse now vanish in the darkness.

John's Return to the Abbey

When John sees the domain of the abbey
Through the morning haze, his heart is gladdened.
When he arrives, all the brothers gather.
A monk says, "James hath died." There is sadness.

There with Ambrose, John speaks, taciturnly
Of John's ambitious plan and strategy.
To the Abbot, it sounds irrational,
And the outcome, doubtless, disastrous:
John appears on Krislos' burial day,
The very hour when King Akaan orates.
John, armed and riding Bolt O'Wrath, arrayed,
Will boldly take Akaan's mistress away.

The Abbot rehearses it in John's ear,
So ludicrous the plan is–the idea.
They both erupt in laughter, eyes in tears,
What problem could ensue? Who'd interfere?

Ambrose recalls he has some pressing chores,
Attend to the duties he must, of course.
John goes outside to saddle up his horse,
Ride Bolt O'Wrath, the countryside explore.

For months John has desired just this respite,
When he can put cares, everything, aside,
Especially take Bolt O'Wrath, his pride,
Alone, remain in solitude, and ride.

John tracks the place where traders found the stream.
Birds dart as John allows his horse to drink.
Rock cliffs, dense foliage there, many large trees,
Water meanders through a cool ravine.

Refreshing scents waft from the forest floor,
A furtive fox slips through the wild flora.
A copacetic sense of grand rapport
Shares its domestic peace, what John came for.

Following downstream, a lengthy distance,
He halts, pondering all, then continues
Through a narrow pass, somewhat restrictive.
In awe, John views a cave with much interest.

He peers inside, allows his eyes to adjust,
To make out the formation as best he could.
The cave seems impressive from where he stood,
Content, John makes his way back from the woods.

Krislos' Execution

Krislos receives his last portion of food,
Served by the captive maid Akaan approved.
She peers into the eyes of the accused,
As sympathy constrains, her tears ensue.

He says, "I bear guilt, o'er this I preside.
I grieve for the Kingdom, all who died,
Yea, and to me, God's judgment hath come nigh,
My nation hath fallen, in ruin lieth."

"My king, thou hast excelled with rare courage,
In bold battle and in raging skirmish,
And faithful to render selfless service,
Blessed art thou and thy holy purpose.

My lord, it is with life I face defeat.
Akaan hath forced me in his bed to sleep.
By King Akaan, a child I have conceived.
So thus, beyond sorrow for thee, I weep.

To this wretched tower, I have been sent,
So rumors shall be spread, Akaan's intent,
To say this child is thine, this to invent,
Thus to harm thee, I do not rest content.

I, Rebekah, wouldst not join with plotters,
I pray, bear thee well, grant me thy pardon,
Since this message shall deepen thy sorrow,
And needlessly bring on thee dishonor."

Her young face is laced with tears as she bows,
"Allow me, my king, to take thy hand now,
To kiss, to banish shame poised o'er thy brow.
Respect I hold for thee, none canst disavow.

What Akaan hath touched, I wouldst destroy.
My womb is filled, but my heart is void.
I plead for wisdom, I must make a choice.
Would that Akaan's low scheme wert quickly foiled.

As bitter as wormwood, my womb burneth,
A hot cauldron that fumeth and stirreth.
Akaan's detested seed in me is nourished,
Doth desecrate what shouldst not be a curse.

At thy dark grave to mourn thee I must be.
What king hath not his vassal or his liege,
At his gravesite to copiously weep,
Except for despots rendered no true grief?

After which I shall succumb in some way,
I to yield to earth's most cruel of days,
Witch's brew ingest, the child's life to take,
Then, tearlessness shall turn me from its grave!"

Would that a noble child wert born to thee,
And I, metamorphic, couldst be thy queen.
Worm to a monarch, a transformation, see.
Idyll days, not few, chronicled wouldst be."

"Rebekah, let right thought purge thy cold heart.
That chaste passion rebuke the witch's arts.
Let thy womb agree and thy heart regard.
Cherish new life, long not for it to part."

"Your Grace, platitudes will ne'er give me rest,
In my womb, two kings war, scandal I wrest.
One deserveth life, one deserveth death,
One wouldst liberate, the other oppress."

He said, "When thy spoiled womb in death hath dealt,
Thine emptiness shall be e'en greater felt,
As heart and body art the more bereft,
Until thy days shall end, thou shall have wept.

All life hath one Creator, Christ of God.
If God made thee, to whom dost thou belong?"
She said, "By Christ, twice acquired, twice begot,
Once by creation, once by ransom bought." (1 Cor 6:20)

Krislos continues, "Thou hast spoken well.
Likewise, the child is God's of life availed.
Its life, though innocent, thou wouldst curtail,
Nor celebrate its life, nor once regale?

For me to help thee wouldst be incumbent.
That my subjects follow and not stumble.
At this late hour, thou dost make me humble.
My hope wast but to leave earth triumphant."

The great bells roar as thunder passing o'er,
Sound dissonant, the waves metallic roar,
Antithesis of song, the heave doth pour,
A malevolent wail from Hell's own source.

Red swirls of wine reflect him in deep thought
As Krislos holds the cup, the taste of gall.
"O'er me a curdling shadow cold, doth fall,
A sadness deep consumeth me, my God."

Krislos finds himself standing by four guards,
He is led from the tower to the yard,
The gallows stand arranged below an arch,
A spectacle misconstrued as mere art.

The idle shadow of the gallows casts,
The soundless silhouette of him, alas,
As silent as a slain Passover lamb,
Its dolor o'er her muted figure passed.

Rebekah Attends Krislos' Corpse

Rebekah weeps as she unfolds the cloth
Bearing the trauma and the grievous loss,
Then proceeding, the shroud is drawn across,
From his feet to his head, she drapes the pall.

"My King, let not Death say, 'Be thou fulfilled.'
Nor charm thy soul to fly off to the hills,
Nor Death, holding thee, claim it is thy will.
But let thy soul resist, be fighting still.

Though in truth, all mortals concede to sleep,
May the shroud bequeath the most restful dream,
And in ecstasy evermore hold thee,
Go thou, my beloved king, in perfect peace."

Wordless echoes against the walls of stone,
Punish the grieved heart dilated alone,
Sentiment of the heartless rock intoned,
Eliciting the tear, the sob, the moan.

Ask how the cross itself doth render peace.
Acquainted, Christ alone, with every grief,
Doth ever of redemption never cease,
This 'Branch' superlative of Eden's trees.

On the cross, the tortured Savior dieth;
Placed within the tomb, His body lieth.
According to the word He prophesieth:
As on the third day, the Lord Christ riseth.

Rebekah melts beneath a hallowed glow,
As intense as the sun, the light did grow!
Not bizarre, but gloriously, it shone,
Extinguishing that same instant of its own.

Her head is on her knees, face on her lap,
As herein ineffability and doubt
Wrestle for her mind in frightful combat,
Thoughts strive within her in vivid contrast.

Then, the all-glorious light illumined
A figure, the aspect of a human,
Whether by eye or divine acumen,
She saw Krislos, and new life imbued him.

Her actions, jubilation, and surprise,
The ecstatic joy flowing from her eyes,
Awakens response on his face besides,
He is puzzled 'til the truth is surmised.

The two hear the prison keeper approach,
He pauses at their door, which still is closed.
The shroud is quickly drawn back o'er Krislos,
And he lies on the bier in strict repose.

Kindness is shown by the jailer, Estaan,
Who speaks: "Krislos' subjects art few at hand
To bury him as his station demands,
Thou must serve me by devising a plan.

For gaolers observe the laws of the court
To expeditiously bury a corpse.
Now thou, Rebekah, must work in due course,
Its fate is in thy hands and thy cohorts."

She asks, "What cohorts have I in prison?"
He responds, "One, the wife of Duke Haslim.
She, as thou, wast brought from a great distance.
She shall meet with thee when she is bidden.

I shall arrange a meeting tomorrow.
Hearing of Krislos, she is in sorrow,
Nothing else in captivity daunts her,
The Duchess shall see thee in short order.

Yet, in this one thing, thou shall have no voice,
The place of burial is Akaan's choice.
The Necropolis, 'City of Gargoyle.'
For kings, he deposes, mocks, and destroys.

She will inform thee of all the others,
I must not name them or tell of their number.
They wert brought here for one reason or another,
They, the elite, for whom Akaan hunted."

The tall, commanding, businesslike Duchess
Enters the vault where Krislos is now kept.
"Purpose of day doth convene us," she says,
In a direct manner, signally correct.

Brashly, she turns and lifts the shroud away,
Krislos lies motionless in a deathlike state.
She wheels around to Rebekah to say,
"Thou must have the King's corpse dressed for the grave."

Rebekah's eyes reflect fear, then relief,
Krislos is being awakened from sleep.
The Duchess, unaware, is now appeased,
Rebekah little notices her leave.

Is this scene a dream or an apparition?
She feels faint, but her true apprehension
Brings to herself its own intervention.
Krislos rises to give her attention.

Krislos catches her as Rebekah swoons.
She lies unconscious there the morning through.
Her eyelids part: she looks about the room
With no recall of those she ever knew.

A knock at the door has been unanswered,
Krislos in the anteroom moves backwards,
Lies upon the bier without distraction,
Pulls the folded shroud, re-draping after.

Rebekah, dazed, confused, opens the door.
The Duchess speaks abruptly as before.
"I have come to remove King Krislos' corpse,
The funeral shall proceed in the morn."

Rebekah strives to keep mental control,
To reconcile events seems beyond hope.
She thinks, "If he is dead, how shall I cope?
But if alive, what shall the future hold?"

The Funeral Procession

Akaan's officers lead on their horses,
Fore and aft, spearmen march with the cortege,
The body is dutifully escorted
To its burial site, thus purported.

The Duchess strolls in her elegiac black,
Gusts of wind unfurl the cape on her back.
The long dress trails loosely below the sash.
The other mourners follow in her tracks.

Rebekah, close behind, anxious, upset,
Wishing this surreal day she could forget.
Macabre, irrational thoughts beset,
Reason must rule her mind despite the rest.

The city of Gargoyle, the 'place of the dead,'
Appears before them to which they are led.
Priests in black garments, red bands on their heads,
Open the gates, incantations are said.

One mourner leaning toward another says,
"Would he hadst escaped, this we detest.
He wast a noble king, may his soul find rest."
The other nods, "He hath too soon met death."

For every worthless briar, thorn, and vine,
Behold where the slumbering plow lieth,
And where in repose is the unmanned scythe,
Fearless, they seize the blades to faultless bind.

Akaan arrives, "Ye citizens elite,
And all my captive enemies now see,
The King of Salem lies at Akaan's feet.
May nothing quench the glory of my speech."

The Magistrate bows to Akaan at once,
After much fanfare, flattery, and pomp.
Lavishly praising the deeds of Akaan,
He gives tribute to Akaan's last triumph.

Akaan comes forth to bring an oration,
Views the obelisk carved for the nation,
Words of the conquest of Krislos at Salem,
As Krislos lies in state there before him.

"All men prosper when my name they exalt,
In battle cry or in triumphant song.
Mine officers and troops in campaign laud.
Who wouldst fail to honor me, great or small?

O Krislos, art there kings greater than I?
Do I not defeat all with whom I vie?
This thou canst not refute nor truth deny.
Praise due Akaan, none giving go awry.

The dying rally at my name in psalm,
Instant sweet is it on the lips of gods.
Craftsmen immortalize it cast in bronze,
Yea, envied is the glory of Akaan.

All know the sting that Akaan canst inflict,
As scorpions disable enemies.
His mighty forces no one canst resist,
Thus, all the nations cower and submit."

Krislos involuntarily twitches,
Immense power to rise surges through him.
His whole frame, musculature, live tissue
Bring him to his feet, as all bear witness.

Gruesome terror has the crowd in its grip.
Terrified, Akaan's limbs quake beneath him,
Rebekah is regaining her senses,
Shock and trauma cause her to reminisce.

The Duchess drops her arms limply and faints,
Her eyes roll back in her head as she wanes.
Attended, her consciousness is regained.
The scene around her cannot be explained.

Wrath for unholy pride is now aroused.
Divine judgment befalls the haughty proud.
"Officers, take charge quickly!" Anwar shouts.
Weapons at Krislos aimed, all swords unhoused.

Krislos' Escape

John sees a chance to help Krislos escape.
The disguise of John's armor, yet in place,
Riding Bolt O'Wrath, he enters the fray,
The crowd, seeing the great horse, makes way.

Rebekah, noting John move through the crowd,
Wondering why he is moving about,
Senses John's intentions–figures it out.
She races toward him as John then dismounts.

The guards notice and instinctively act.
Krislos suddenly pulls straight from their grasp,
Then leaping from the wall, mounts Bolt O'Wrath.
John helps Rebekah to mount at the back.

A short bow is fired; the arrow strikes her.
Her body, shocked, as she takes the arrow.
Rebekah is slumping, leaning forward.
John is crazed, not believing the horror.

Rebekah looks at John to catch his eye,
That all meaning might pass, be realized,
Of words not spoken, ne'er could e'er disguise,
"Thou I praise, I thank thee. I bid goodbye."

Krislos and John turn her body around
To be held by Krislos in front, to mount.
Krislos orders the exiles from the crowd
To follow him, "Get up quickly!" he shouts.

John turns with arrow plucked from his quiver,
Draws on his bow, aiming, he delivers.
The missile flies with speed invisible
Sunders Rau's breastplate, to the heart enters.

John's bold archenemy drops off the horse,
With the deadly shaft of the arrow borne
To its mark, for its cause, spent as John swore,
Alas, this fails her, and torments John the more.

The Duchess, standing a few feet from Rau,
Appalled, alarmed, sees Rau clutching the shroud.
It matters not why he has it, nor how,
She pulls it from his grasp when he falls down.

John, pulling Rau's boot loose from the stirrup,
Then, taking the horse, cinching the girth up,
Mounts the stallion, just ready to spur him.
The Duchess cries to John to help her up.

Seated behind John, she holds fast to the shroud.
The exiles take steeds released by the crowd.
Krislos leading them, they make their way out
To seek a place of refuge, they are bound.

Rebekah's blood has pooled on Krislos' clothes.
He soon will place her body in repose.
The river that passes through Pross, he knows
Will give the tired exiles rest from their woes.

The few exiles now settle in the camp,
Gently, Rebekah's body is laid down,
Victor, an exile, takes the arrow out.
Krislos has women cleanse her and her gown.

Rebekah's Wake Begins
John's loss, the disappointment is so deep,
Seeing her desperation, close was he;
Despair is so profound he cannot speak.
Morose bewilderment is smothering.

John stands close to Rebekah's wake, grieving.
Her loss of life, his quest, or its reason,
He struggles to grasp the why–the meaning.
Again, remorse rushes o'er his being.

Elaam and Hector Escape Pross

The Emir governs in the King's absence,
Responsible for all civil matters.
A sentry comes racing to the palace,
"Emir! There's been an escape of the captives!

No one couldst stop them, King Krislos escaped!
A knight on horseback helped him break away.
Give us thine orders, we have been betrayed!"
Elaam shouts, "Send every guard to the fray!"

Akaan in Denial

Akaan is fuming, expressing his wrath,
"Krislos feigned death as a master plan!
There wast no corpse as a funeral hath,
The shroud hid him, under our nose he passed!"

Akaan Pursues Elaam

"The Emir I condemn, this cursed Elaam,
Spy and traitor to Akaan and Kingdom.
His blood with Salemites co-mingled,
Go, find the Emir! No longer linger!"

To find Elaam, Akaan sends a cohort.
They go straight to Pross to search his quarters.
Throughout the city, the walls, it borders,
Pursuits fail. He gives no further orders.

Krislos Speaks at Rebekah's Wake

As one in sacred sleep, Rebekah rests.
Two raven locks combed from the back of her head,
Drawn forth o'er her shoulders, upon her breasts,
Embosom the bright cross about her neck.

"Thy blood streamed rivulet as to the sea.
Thy queenly aspect feign wouldst death appease.
Well might thine eyes decline that they not see
How thy fair veins outpoured unworthily.

Our Christ didst of His own fount give away,
Swear by thy lifeless lips the chalice take,
Pray that His dispensation thou partake
Of resurrection life that thou awake."

The Duchess steps forward as Krislos talks,
As if bearing an oblation, she walks
With reverence, the shroud to him is brought.
The King, faintly smiling, accepts the cloth.

Krislos beholds her most exquisite face,
Forehead to chin, rare in the human race,
Her neck and body, all proportionate,
The shroud across her precious body lay.

The exiles view the scene: this holy act.
The shroud illuminates them, light is cast.
Her body rises free, the shroud unwraps.
She stands cloaked with full radiance, unmasked.

All are astonished; they cannot relate.
Exulting, all watch, surprised and amazed.
Rebekah looks upward with hands upraised,
She beautifully offers a song of praise.

Exodus from Pross

That night, exiles come out to celebrate.
They remain awed at what has taken place.
"Krislos and Rebekah to life art raised!
And we, liberated from Pross, escaped!"

They fixate on Krislos, ebullient,
Animate that 'Our King is among us!'
John shall speak with him of their exodus.
He comes before the King with deference.

 The King is aware: "John is my name, my lord."
"As I gather," said Krislos, "Our hero."
"O King, I knew not I'd rescue ye both,
But 'twas a work of God, the Lord of Hosts.

Now I see clearly 'twas God's intention,
For the Kingdom's sake, God's intervention.
An outcome with divine consequences.
Pray God will grant me more of His wisdom."

"John, I wilt have thee lead, call men to arms."
Observing Krislos and his scars of war,
From what John can see, he suffered much harm.
"My King, I have no war honors, no scars."

Krislos replies, "Scars mark us as they must,
Thy worthiness standeth, if war be just.
The battles wilt be severe before us.
He concludes, "Scars follow the courageous."

"May scars derive from worthy wounds, my lord,
Nor may imprudence wield an unproved sword."
Quoth Krislos, "Behold the Emperor of woe...
Gaze into His wounds and heal thine own." (C. H. Spurgeon)

Exodus to the Monastery

In the night, John's startled; he's alerted,
His name is whispered–it's disconcerting.
Elaam and Hector have the camp stirring,
John said, "These men art friends, do not worry!"

When John, Hector, and Elaam, deliberate,
They draw aside while the other folk wait.
What John told Krislos, he reiterates,
The King, from the exiles, must separate.

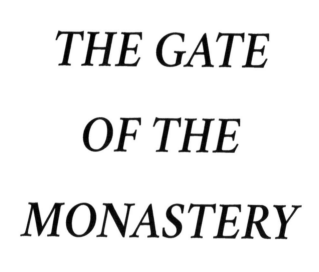

THE GATE

OF THE

MONASTERY

John Provides Seclusion for Krislos' Safety
John gives thought to where Krislos should remain.
The monastery shall not be the place,
For secrecy there could not be sustained.
John concludes he should occupy the cave.

The cave's detriment is its attribute,
Isolated, though not far to commute
To where faithful subjects can relate news,
Information gained at the travel route.

Cover is the cave's critical feature,
The King's location must be kept secret.
King Krislos can strategize discreetly,
Separation from folk is essential.

"My lord, a secure place I've found at last,
A special area, safe from attack.
Only three of us wouldst be the contacts,
Myself, Hector, and Elaam know this, in fact.

My lord, no other place couldst I provide
Accommodation for thee to survive.
The Abbot must know that we have arrived
For the present source of food and supplies."

"Go set it up now, tonight," said the King.
"My work for the Kingdom there, needeth be.
What way wouldst Elaam be auspice to me?"
"War consultant," John said, "Faithful to thee."

The Shroud at the Monastery

The Abbot Ambrose is walking about,
Ruminating and struggling with his doubts
Of what the exiles testify about.
'We have seen King Krislos, he's with us now.'

The Abbot wants most to see and believe.
The Duchess is quite credible indeed,
"I wast standing by the bier within reach,
When Krislos rose, and from his captors broke free."

All heads are turning toward Rebekah now.
She strode to the votive table of prayer,
Unfolding the cloth, the full length of the shroud.
Ambrose, monks, and subjects gather around.

"This is the shroud of Jesus Christ our Lord!"
In awe, they step back as their prayers go forth,
From veneration springs weeping for joy,
Whispers o'erheard, "This is Christ's blood, adored!"

She said, "Behold, Christ's image on the shroud
Thus doth portray His resurrection power.
I wast slain by an enemy's arrow,
But raised to life, the Savior didst endow.

By crucifixion, nails and spear pierced through.
Jesus on the cross they didst execute.
Christ wast buried but arose from the tomb.
The Shroud of Turin, bloodstained from His wounds."

King Krislos, unnoticed, has since arrived.
Also, with the King, John is standing by,
For minutes, observing there from behind.
John announces, "King Krislos is alive!"

The King's Admonishment Regarding the Shroud

They shout, "Hail to the King, long live the King!
Long live Rebekah." There is rejoicing.
King Krislos graciously decides to speak.
"And long live ye people of the Kingdom!

Abbot Ambrose, devout monks. For subjects,
The Monastery gates opened for us.
Thy doors, thy sanctuary, received us,
Despite the dangers now threatening us.

Akaan hath eyed the shroud, for it may search.
Perhaps he'd fancy it for magic works.
Abbot Ambrose knoweth its sacred worth,
The shroud, the monastery must conserve."

John speaks with the Abbot

John said to Ambrose, "We impose on thee,
Our hope is for survivability."
The Abbot replied, "We honor the King.
Our endeavor shall be how best serve ye."

John spoke, "To accommodate us, indeed,
Our alms shall be sufficient for our keep.
Our burden to thee, substantial may be,
But the subjects shall serve to relieve thee.

Of this matter, dear Abbot, thou shouldst know,
I shall provide lodging for King Krislos,
But I must ask thee for his provisions."
He said, "Amenities, he shall lack none."

"Abbot, I must speak now with the Duchess."
The Abbot stepped aside courteously.
"Kind madam, I owe Duke Haslim a debt."
"A debt? How canst that be?" asks the Duchess.

"From Salem to Pross, I wast journeying.
It so happened, whilst the Duke wast hunting,
His horse kicked and disabled the hunter,
I, perchance, heard his cry at that juncture.

Next, at the castle, he wast quite distraught.
Whilst I was there, he spoke of thee at Pross,
With endearment, deploring thy cruel bonds,
Asked, when I go there, to learn of thy want.

Hoping his message wouldst reach his beloved,
Paid me to take this letter of comfort."
John hears the quiet sobs of the Duchess,
Long pent-up passion unleashed like a flood.

"To Salem, I am bound, time draweth near.
Thou mayest reply, prepare, whilst I'm here."
She pens with a lovely flourish of the quill,
Her experiences and her love, sincere.

Krislos, John, and Elaam at the Cave

John and Elaam meet in the early morn
At the cave, with Krislos, breakfast before.
Each anticipates they will discuss war.
Krislos wants to hear from Elaam much more.

"What wast thy mission at Salem, Emir?"
"Akaan hadst me secure Salem's treasury
To fund the war, conducted by the Princes."
Krislos motioned, "Please continue, indeed.

Didst thou secure it prior to injury?"
"I secured it and inventoried it."
"Doth Akaan know where it is presently?"
"Aye, the treasury is in jeopardy.

Akaan didst know he couldst not trust Princes.
When he thought I wast dead he withdrew them.
Treasury found wouldst start war amongst them.
His army couldst not be saved, nor save him."

"At Pross, didst thou have treasury control?"
"Aye, as head of revenue, it is so."
"John, to muster our troops, what dost thou know?"
"My lord, 'twouldst be what the King proposeth."

Krislos said, "In Haslim, thou must confide.
Learn of my army and of our allies,
And speak to him to inform me of knights,
How many known in the kingdom reside."

"I have a kinsman in knighthood, my lord.
His name is Bertrand, in the kingdom's north."
"I know him, the Prince of Knights," said Krislos.
"Conscript Bertrand for service, my orders!

Emir, how many o'er Salem stand guard?"
"Akaan's Sultan hath two thousand thus far."
Krislos said, "The treasury is yet ours,
With which we'll adequately finance the war.

The Sultan's forces thou shall lure away.
They do not know of thy recent escape.
Go, order them now to evacuate,
After which thou shall conduct a swift raid."

From the King, Elaam requests some parchment,
Drafts a military order proper,
With the Emir's seal, 'Order of Akaan,'
Addresses it to the Sultan, Bazran.

"John, thou and Elaam must depart in haste,
But ride apart, keep some distance away.
Ye must not be seen as associates,
Lest a report of ye causes this to fail.

Godspeed, Elaam, meeting with the Sultan.
If all goes well, then reunite with John,
Head north, meet with Earl Raulf and with Bertrand.
Plan the raid well in secret discussions."

THE SULTAN'S

GATE

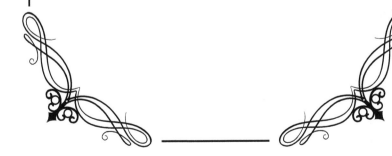

The Sultan's Gate

To Salem, the Emir boldly rides forth,
"A dignitary!" the sentry reports,
Gates are opened by official order.
He is welcomed to the Sultan's quarters.

The Sultan receives the dignitary.
Great smiles and greetings are reciprocated.
Officers resume work designated.
The servants bring ale and delicacies.

Bazran's mien displays curiosity.
Elaam expects an interrogative,
Thus, he hands the sealed order to Bazran,
Who separates the seal of the parchment.

His eyes follow each line of the edict,
Perplexed, the Sultan looks up at Elaam.
Elaam states, "I am here to apprise thee
What Akaan's intentions for Salem be."

"What art these intentions?" the Sultan asks.
"Utter destruction!" The Emir's eyes flash.
"Akaan wilt dispossess all Salemites,
Every village shall belch out smoke and ash!"

"Then why this order to deploy to Pross?"
With firmness, the Emir swears, "For this cause,
Thou shall lead all Akaan's forces, at large,
Akaan's army hath been put in thy charge."

"One last question," the Sultan asks, "Why me?"
Emir Elaam pauses, "No one but thee!
Every inch of this land is known to thee,
No regiment fights independently.

The King sleeps not until Salem's destroyed!
He doth muster coalition forces.
Waste no time to act on this deployment.
Akaan wilt see thy face in a fortnight."

John and Bertrand Meet Haslim at the Castle

A lively page enters to see Haslim
To announce the arrival of two men.
"Lad, who art the guests here thou dost mention?"
"Sir, a knight, and the other is Ekraam."

There's a rather prompt response from the Duke.
"Receive them, bring them to the drawing room,
Tell Gellett to serve them some food and brew."
Ekraam he knows, and knights he knows a few.

"Ah! The Prince of Knights, I'm honored, Bertrand!"
"As am I, by thy sponsored tournaments."
"Welcome to thee, and of course, thou Ekraam.
Please be seated and enjoy refreshments."

John hands Haslim the Duchess's sought letter,
Written by her own hand, most coveted.
"As I promised," John said, "As directed."
The Duke's eyes grow moist, joy effervescing.

Taking it aside, blithefully he reads.
The Duke, incredulous, can hardly speak,
Haslim, turning to John, is very pleased,
"I thank thee, thou hast kept thy word to me."

The Duke said, "Let us have a discussion.
Ekraam, thou dost rove with two escutcheons,
Necor's, not Krislos', wast my assumption."
"Aye Duke, I shall put to rest that question.

When I first met thee on my way to Pross,
Posing as Necor's officer I wast,
An alias I needed for my cause
To save a captive. My true name is John.

Bertrand is my kinsman, we serve Krislos.
We have come here under Krislos' orders.
We art here seeking to raise forces.
Krislos expects war soon at our borders."

The Duke said, "Hadst the Duchess not told me
Thy story, I wouldst never have believed,
Nor that Krislos couldst have contacted thee
To raise an army for the King, indeed!"

John said, "Albeit, the King hath sent us.
Myself, Bertrand, and Elaam, Krislos trusts
To find men who will fight, bring to muster."
"And to draft stalwart knights," Bertrand asserts.

The Duke's eyebrow is raised, "Emir Elaam!?"
"Aye, he defected, escaped from Akaan.
Elaam wast able to dupe the Sultan,
By ruse, and return his regiments to Pross.

Elaam, by Krislos' orders, furthermore,
Sacked Salem's treasury to finance the war."
Haslim's eyebrows are knit, "Strap on thy swords!
Heavens! Let us prepare for all-out war!

Our King and noblemen must now congress.
Threat and fear of war must not confound us,
We must find, marshall the flagging army,
Empower, weaponize them to conquer!"

Krislos and Hector, at the Cave
Outside the cave, Hector takes a slow walk.
The cliff might provide good views from the top,
Krislos is by the stream for fresh water.
As Hector peers upward, the King watches.

"Go up for observation," the King said.
Hector scales the challenging cliff to check.
He finally reaches the stony crest.
The bright sun highlights the monastery.

The long highway can be viewed from this spot,
For surveillance, it could benefit a lot
To monitor traffic to or from Pross.
He is prepared to inform King Krislos.

Hector descends carefully, he strolls back,
Chewing a twig, removes it casually.
"O King, it's good!" "The twig?" Krislos asks him.
"No lord, to see the road, all that passes.

The monastery and the long highway,
Lord the King, I can see five miles each way."
"That shouldst prove very helpful," Krislos said.
"Keep me informed of the traffic each day."

"My lord, hold this not against me, prithee,
Of my last trip to the monastery..."
"Say on, Hector." "Rebekah, the lady,
I dare say it is so, with child is she!"

Krislos hesitates, "It is Akaan's child.
Thou knowest she wast entrapped, 'twas her plight.
There couldst be much talk, let it not be thine,
Except when thou speakest truth, be not blind."

"King, who wilt help her now in such a plight?
How canst she alone face this in her life?"
"Thou art wise, Hector, much wiser than I,
It is the King who lacketh the eyesight.

This issue, Ambrose and I wilt address.
We wilt determine a course of action
To confront any false accusations.
But she beareth no guilt as imagined."

Exiles at the Monastery

Conception is evident, by her womb.
Rebekah and the child suffered mortal wounds.
From death, both were raised, both were spared the tomb.
Her confidante must give her counsel soon.

Rebekah is alert, fully woken,
She feels movement low in her abdomen.
Strangely, she is startled: 'life' she's holding,
Alive to that which makes disconsolate.

Rebekah and Julia

On their daily walk, she and Julia talk.
"Rebekah, I see, thou art in despond
O'er the child, verily, thou art."
"Julia, my concerns, two-fold, two apart;

They art for the child's welfare, and my sake.
As shame doth birth its offspring in disgrace
With reality's conspicuous face,
I do fear how this birth shall be portrayed."

Julia, seen as wise in her comportment
Has grown steadfast in Rebekah's support.
She finds Julia's friendship quite important,
Her counsel is honest and proportionate.

"Perception hath no loyalty to truth,
Nor doth opinion, allegation, rumor.
A gossip feedeth those wont to accuse,
Innocence heard last, guilt then, first assumed.

Rebekah, who loyal to thee canst speak?
Who knoweth all the facts concerning thee?"
Rebekah thought, "The King, John and Elaam."
"Then God for thee, who opposed canst succeed?"

A Delegation Meets Krislos

A rumble grows resoundingly distinct,
Sounds of horses, while not yet appearing,
Heard at the monastery–they're nearing,
The drama of hoofbeats nearly ceasing.

Down from the cliff to Krislos comes Hector.
"John, two others, many knights here headed!"
For King Krislos, this is unexpected,
John, Haslim, Bertrand, he'll be receptive.

As such, Krislos, acknowledging the three,
"Ye have come with a knight in company.
Bertrand, the King hath seen impressive feats."
"For the King and for the Kingdom," said he.

Krislos nods, "Ye all have come here boldly."
"Aye," Haslim speaks, "If thou wilt, King Krislos,
Allow us to present plans which art bold.
Stark events compel us now to do so.

We've met with nobles and Salem's leaders,
Desiring to bring thee back, we're eager.
Bozran deploys troops to Pross, we're seeing.
An imminent attack we art fearing.

Akaan's forces wilt be heavily armed,
And with allies wouldst be preponderant.
God, foreknowing, raised thee by His strong arm.
We need thee, O King, as we art alarmed."

"Bold thou art," said Krislos, "Art ye able
To conduct exiles and the King safely?"
Bertrand replies, "To take ye to Salem,
One hundred knights art standing by, waiting."

All Meet at the Monastery

Both the Duke and Duchess are ecstatic,
Love's celebration and its contagion
Has stirred every soul throughout the Abbey,
Smiling broadly with all is the Abbot.

John, absorbed, sees a lovely young woman.
Accordingly, she's poised and elegant,
And with graceful, genteel aspect of one,
Rebekah, jubilant, rises and walks toward John.

She extends both hands; he holds both with pride.
Myriad memories pass through their minds.
"Thou didst risk thy life for me John, but why?"
They stand face-to-face, questions in her eyes.

"Harm that wast done to thee, I wouldst reverse,
Freedom from rapacity thou deserved."
"John, my life thou didst save, my life preserve."
"Rest, a queen's title upon thee wouldst serve.

I shall call thee Queen," John said casually.
She jesting, "Doth the King know?" they're laughing.
"Note, I'm pregnant with Akaan's child, alas.
Whose queen shall I be?" wistfully, she asks.

"Of thee," John said, "Akaan is not worthy.
One worthy of thee, there is one only."
Julia, a fugitive, enters with tea.
John, acknowledging, stands courteously.

John's Acquaintance with Julia

John is captivated by her beauty.
She smiles, "Wouldst thou join us now and have tea?"
John is distracted, "Have tea?" she repeats.
"Oh quite, oh aye, of course, I shall indeed."

Hilarity chokes them at John's unease.
John says, "Occasion lacked for us to meet."
"I'm Julia. Thy brave rescue set us free.
Thou didst secure our kingdom, thankfully.

Or else, King and Kingdom couldst have been lost."
"Aye, thankfully," said John. "Glory to God;
Incalculable wouldst have been the loss,
If forfeiture of hope hadst been our lot.

Now situate we art in warfare's throes,
Again, in fact, the Kingdom is exposed.
Salem urgently calleth for Krislos
To commandeer assumption of the throne.

His going shall include us fugitives.
Make preparations for leaving forthwith,
A wagon ye shall have to travel in.
With little delay, the trip shall commence."

Krislos and Subjects Depart to Salem

Krislos is ready to inform, remarking,
"Dear Abbot, monks of the monastery,
Now the time is here for our departure,
To restore at Salem the monarchy.

With these here, supporting this endeavor.
Alms and largesse, though with ample treasure,
Couldst not express our gratitude, ever.
The debt we owe ye is without measure."

Ambrose speaks, "As measureless as debts be,
And thy gifts weighed, insufficient wouldst be,
Lo, paupers we both be, save for God's strength.
Didst Thomas A Kempis not say, indeed?

'Love feeleth no burden
thinketh nothing of trouble
attempteth what is above strength...
where he doth not love wouldst faint and lie down.'
(Thomas A Kempis)

We honor thee, O King, bid thee Godspeed."
"Amen," the hosts say, "And to those with thee.
Our prayers we offer to God for all ye,
To prosper the Kingdom, the Crown and King."

John and Julia at the Castle

At the castle one balmy afternoon,
John listens to an ethereal tune,
Transient from the cloister chapel room.
John is spellbound as Julia plays her flute.

"Whilst passing by, I heard such divine notes,
I wast impressed by the exposition,
And enthralled by the charm thy flute evokes.
Wouldst thou join me outdoors for a short stroll?"

She's pleased, "I'd be delighted, thou art kind."
They exit the castle in bright sunshine.
"I shall hold this blissful day in my mind,"
John said, "Capture this rare moment in time."

Julia asks, "Concerning war, dost thou fear?"
John says, "I know fighting though not warfare.
Soon, I'll measure the enemy's fierceness.
I pray twice the prowess to wield the spear.

I fear a loss of life for those with no swords,
Those in the path of pitiless hordes.
Julia, of war, I dreamt a short time ago,
Shall I tell thee the dream?" She said, "Do so."

John's Dream of War

"In the dream, afar, I saw light aglint.
On a mountain, one calleth me to him.
I, off my horse, on through the forest went,
Then I climbed straight up the mountain ascent.

One sat with me, my angst o'er war discussed,
For as yet, I hadst no good plan to trust,
I, by this host, who to me speaking thus,
War strategy, as wast seen from above.

The countryside of Salem is ablaze,
The great army seeth smoke when they invade,
Having traveled far, the foe is dismayed,
No spoil, no food, nor captives there to take.

I wast intrigued, so down on this, I looked.
Below, two armies, one with great fear shook,
This one, better armed, their weapons forsook,
The other seized these weapons, all they took.

I see the forces which left Pross, art large,
Forces remaining at Pross, few in charge.
Krislos, by stealth, arriveth there, well-armed,
He spoiled Pross, then it's set on fire at large."

Julia asks, "Hast thou confidence in such?"
"The dream hath merit," says John, "Shouldst I trust?
It is a dream with little to discuss.
If it be prophetic, 'twould be worth much."

John Expresses His Admiration for Julia

"A premonition of thee, heav'n given,
Didst arrest my thought that thou existed,
For now, mine eye doth behold thine image.
When first I saw thee, my heart wast smitten.

A specter rayed through prism's sapphire eye,
Didst awe my gaze, to know thee, my desire.
Lest love, late-spoken, sullen, go awry.
May my candor not daunt thee nor give thee fright."

"John, as for zeal, may ardor quench a fault!
For we have scarcely met, thus thou dost talk?
And is war's strategy how love is sought?
I trust sincerity speaketh what ought."

"Julia, may charity rule my candor.
Prithee, my awkward wooing be pardoned,
That my love as sincere be regarded,
But thy decorum hath quenched my ardor."

"Tis better to be vile than vile esteem'd,
When not to be receives reproach of being,
And the just pleasure lost which is so deem'd."
(Excerpt from Shakespeare's Sonnet CXXL)

THE GATE

OF PROSS

UNLOCKED

War Strategy

War strategy, Krislos must now discuss.
The King considers few comitatus,
Haslim, John, Elaam, and Bertrand he can trust,
Just three, he will bring in now to consult.

"The gravity of this war, ye men know,
We must war with a preponderant foe,
Perhaps the size of ten-to-one ratio.
We must deal with that ratio with the bow.

Krislos questions, "What dost thou proffer, John?"
John speaks, "When we face forces of Akaan,
There wilt be fewer troops at Pross on guard,
Counterattack, make our assault on Pross.

We will set the city of Pross afire,
We'll break Akaan's momentum when he strikes.
Akaan, with fury, will head back to fight,
We'll engage at Pross when he arriveth."

"Elaam, what is thy strategy?" he asks.
"Counterattack, according to John's plan,
Akaan is apt to split his troops in half,
Strike Salem's north, strike Salem's south, both paths.

A third route he'll avoid, between the two,
The middle route, though tortuous, we'll use.
We wilt, as well, in half divide our troops,
One half, I'll lead through Pross' middle route."

Bertrand asks, "Why wouldst thou do this Elaam?
Thou art from Pross, one of Akaan's elite."
Elaam said, "My life King Akaan doth seek.
Converted wast I to see as thou see'st."

John said, "Aye, all the more, he'll want thee slain,
With a great bounty on thy head and name."
"Nevertheless," said Elaam, "I'm constrained.
My strategy, I shall further explain.

Beneath the city, broad tunnels exist,
Hidden outside, an access leadeth in.
Once in, we wilt unlock the gates from within.
Our troops, readied, incursion wilt begin.

The prison doors we'll open, free each man,
Defeat and plunder Pross as fast as we can,
Of treasure, food, and weapons, as I've planned,
Hide them as I direct, set Pross aflame."

"Bertrand, what is thy plan and strategy?"
"I support, O King, their plans for battle.
Their plans I wilt sanction, with this added,
Deploy on Salem's front, troops, other half.

Across two routes, the north and south set stakes,
To slow Akaan's advance when he invades.
When stalled, archers will fiercely strike his flanks,
From Salem's troops positioned in advance.

If the foe's troops from the west strike Salem,
Our troops pivot to fight the invaders.
Salem's walls canst help thwart the assailants,
Though with fewer troops, we canst engage them.

When Elaam hath accomplished his mission,
He'll join us with his troops, in addition,
With the spoil of Pross in his possession,
Resupply our troops, take up positions."

Krislos says, "Our shore west, requireth ships!
John, what of our floundering fleet exists?
By whose littoral land doth my fleet list?
Sail they? Whose flag? What hath become of it?"

John asks, "Hath the King been told of Milo,
A mercenary with us, dost thou know?
Knowledge of campaigns, warfare he doth show."
The King replies, "I have not yet been told.

Contact the fugitives and have him found."
Milo was presented within the hour.
He stands erect with proper martial air,
"Milo, my lord, at thy service," he bowed.

"Milo, why wouldst thou enlist with Krislos?
No mercenaries have I hired at all."
With a sincere expression, Milo paused,
"A better choice, my lord, to serve thy cause.

I chose not Akaan, I escaped his draft,
He purposed to hold me within his grasp.
With few in number that thy forces have,
I wouldst serve Krislos' cause if thou shouldst ask.

My lord, I have this that I wouldst disclose,
From military conquests," said Milo,
"Often men mused o'er the fate of Krislos,
Men who served King Krislos, I have noted.

Perchance found, wouldst rally in this grave hour
To bring thee battle strength, thou'd be empower'd."
Krislos quickens; optimism rebounds.
"Without delay, seek those thou canst track down!

Milo, seek mine army as directed.
In thy hand thou shall have the King's letter.
Attempt to find the leaders I message.
With thee, I shall send Haslim and Hector."

Haslim, Hector, and Milo at Berlbic's Castle

The three endure a week's grueling travel.
They enter the hall of Berlbic's castle.
Desirous to trace the king's detachments,
To stir allies to act on this matter.

Court jester Ordulf, lithe, elf-like, bobs by.
Brass bells dight pointed hat and shoes alike.
Beneath his hat, thatched hair pokes out, tow-light,
His face is sportive, with green imposing eyes.

Hector learns his name, "How be thou, Ordulf?"
"I be very well."
"'Dost thou know tales of King Krislos' soldiers?'
   Ordulf: "I know tales."
   Hector: "And what tales dost thou know?"
   Ordulf: "I know short tales and long tales;
         short tales worth silver, long tales worth gold;
         for true tales, ye pay more, then more."
   Hector: "Tell us one true tale: where Krislos' soldiers be."
   Ordulf: "One be there, another, there."
         He points to two men chatting with Edred.

Haslim, Hector, and Milo march through the hall.
Edred's elated, Haslim toward him walks.
"Hail, friend! What bringeth Haslim here to call?"
"Much to tell, Edred, much news I have brought.

Edred," Haslim asserts, "We're on a quest;
And who art these two men thou dost address?"
Milo, standing behind Haslim, attests,
"On Edred's right is Whitby; Gibbs, on his left."

Earl Edred queries, "And who mightst thou be?"
"I'm Milo, pardon the intrusion please,
In wars past, Edred, I partnered with these."
Then they exclaim, "Milo!" in disbelief.

"In the council room, early tomorrow,
Says Edred, "Requisite that we parley
With Duke Berlbic and nobles regarded."
Haslim, Hector, and Milo are enheartened.

The three, once more, return to see Ordulf.
"For thy true tale, Ordulf, thou didst earn gold."
Ordulf deftly snaps up what Haslim holds.
"Cock-a-hoop!" Ordulf leaps off with a song:

   "I am contented with my store
   Although I should not be the worse
   For just a little more..." (Song, Classic Sea Stories, pg. 602)

Parley at Berlbic's Castle

The parley with compatriots convenes.
"Duke Haslim," Edred says, "We welcome thee.
And, as well, we welcome thy two colleagues.
Of thy concerns, we gladly hear thee speak."

Addressing the assembly, Haslim stands.
"Earl, Duke, nobles, compatriots at hand,
If ye've not heard, Krislos at Pross wast hanged."
Grave concern shows on each face, man to man.

"Miraculously, God restored his life."
Wonderment then changed to relief and sighs.
"The King escaped; his throne he occupies.
Now, we have come to tell of Salem's plight,

Akaan schemes to annihilate our Kingdom!
We have come to warn of war's imminence,
Of the prospect of battles impending,
Krislos is desperate for enlistments,

To seek and restore his army's remnant,
To find the fleet of ships he commissioned,
Gain knowledge of their state and condition.
To seek thine aid, King Krislos hath sent us."

Haslim's succinct appeal did resonate.
For cheerless murmurs swelled from what he spake.
Sober expressions held on their faces.
A baron stands, "Hear, hear ye!" his voice raised.

"What need have we of any rash response?
Against us here, Akaan hath no grievance,
Shouldst a wayward moor stumble upon us,
Our knights defend our shires, in them we trust."

Whitby speaks, known for valor in battle.
"Gentlemen! Believe this news from Haslim!
We must heed and take hold of this matter,
War is at hand, imminent, harrowing!

Akaan wilt supply his army with ships,
We must block him from succeeding in this.
Search harbors, find where Krislos' ships yet list.
Bring up Krislos' fleet, his soldiers therein."

The patriots shout, "Aye, Whitby is right!"
He continues, "Hear ye, now is the time
To say what commitment is to be thine,
Choose who liveth or dieth, thus decide!"

Now Haslim hopes they will commit to fight.
He urges them to join the enterprise,
"Engage! Call men to muster nationwide."
They join the quest with him, and he is surprised.

Duke Berlbic and the earl, taken aback,
"Persuasively thou callest men to act.
Of support, we assure thee, Duke Haslim,
We shall supply men and arms for combat."

"Good, gentlemen! In unity, we stand,
Allied with King Krislos, we'll save our land,"
Says Haslim, "Duty served by every man,
Shall shake Akaan's conquests out of his hands!

Thus, it is now incumbent that we all
Be purveyors of the news, shout abroad:
'We prepare for war, men to arms we call
To save our Homeland, join the Kingdom's cause!'"

"The noble man makes noble plans,
    and by noble deeds he stands." (Isa. 32:8 NIV)

Rebekah Gives Birth

At Haslim's castle, where Julia resides,
She has been summoned to Rebekah's side.
Contractions are not far apart, the sign.
"Send," Julia urges, "Call now the midwife!"

Sublime, the contradiction, all at once,
The sharp audacity of pains affront.
So searing is the agony that comes.
The pain is irreversible till done.

The pain anathema to the joy of birth,
As she has born a son of priceless worth,
That once she thought would constitute a curse,
Now soar toward heaven, praises, not a dirge.
"Only with God's good hand, and strict bridle,
can the soul be helped to give its best."
(Concise Dictionary of Religions Quotations, pg. 66)

Ambitious, Victor and Celia bestir,
Hearing that Rebekah has just given birth.
"Krislos hath sired a newborn son," they smirk,
They disparage King Krislos and besmirch.

Victor says, "Krislos shouldst be enamored."
Celia quips, "'Whose Queen shall I be?' now answered.
He and Rebekah 'raised' in like manner.
'Kindred spirits' art they? Oh, such banter."

Victor and Celia Before Krislos

Enter Victor and Celia, conniving,
Ingratiating, bowing to the King.
"O King," Victor hails, "We bring glad tidings,
Of her, from whom the arrow I excised."

King Krislos, diligently at work, sits.
"I presume the ill-fated one liveth."
"Aye! News of Lady Rebekah, lordship!
Birth to a noble son ere she didst give.

A male child, born to this lovely lady,
The father is unknown, or else, missing.
What wilt be done for her? Such a pity."
For Krislos' comment, they wait intently.

Krislos sees through their sophomoric question.
"About the father, ye art addressing,
Or perhaps, o'er one ye art obsessing,
'What will be done?' What is thy suggestion?"

They glance at one another, and then they speak.
"We think that such a man, we ought to seek."
Krislos asks them, "Finding him, what gain ye?"
They say, "Exposed, he doth deserve to be."

King Krislos says, "Rebekah's quote, ye know,
'Whose Queen shall I be, Akaan's or Krislos'?
Thus, I couldst be impugned by such a quote,
Thus, by one's tongue, my wealth one couldst extort.

Tongue's arrows struck, no man canst e'er remove,
Pierce irretrievably the one they shoot.
The words that slander and the words untrue,
Words unfounded, ignorantly accuse."

They ask, "What if Akaan saith it's not his?"
Saith he, "That doth contradict the evidence.
At my last hour, Rebekah declared this,
Akaan's child she'd conceived, willed death to it."

Victor and Celia, disconcerted, bow.
They are nonplussed but feel not disempowered,
To give Akaan word, 'Thou hast a son now,'
Should ameliorate their future somehow.

Rebekah Announced as Queen

For private counsel, Krislos makes a request.
"Friends, a kingdom wisely ruled endureth,
Thus, to render counsel, I didst select
Thou John, Elaam, Julia, and the Duchess.

The Kingdom shall be enriched as perceived,
Krislos hath chosen Rebekah as Queen,
Subjects loyal to her as to the King.
May her role as the Queen be blessed by thee."

To be Queen, they support that she be named,
Royal robes on the chosen shall be graced.
How shall the child under Krislos be raised?
On the Prince, may robes of honor be laid.

"His name," states Julia, "let it now be known,
Queen Rebekah hath named her son Jerome."
Speaking of him, John and Elaam, intone,
"Prince in two Kingdoms, which throne will he own?"

The Duchess speaks, "Thou King, chose one, thy Queen,
May privilege choose that I christen her,
O King, as well, she be named Christina,
Prepare a royal suite, to esteem her."

Elegantly appointed is the room,
As the fair Duchess would thereof approve,
The windows, facing south, frame sunlit views,
Refreshing air fills out the drapes in plumes.

High-canopied bed with grand ornate posts,
Richly bedraped, drawn back, gird fabric folds.
Soft silken bedding, sumptuous pillows,
Prepared meticulously for repose.

Julia's anticipated visit, late,
Christina hears, in time, a flautist play
As Julia, in procession, comes that way.
Servants bring blooms, extravagant bouquets.

The Duchess and Julia bow to the King;
They exit. "My King!" exclaims Christina,
"I'm speechless, I have no breath for to speak,
The flute, the flowers, thoughtful inquiry!"

The tone of her face changed from mere pallor
To a radiant blush, passion's color.
"I've never seen such love in thine eyes, lord."
He said, "For my love doth exceed all love before."

She glances at the crib, the child asleep.
"My King, I know not what to say of him."
Krislos smiles, "Son of Christina, the Queen."
She gasps, "Thou sayest Christina! The Queen?!

O my King, how shall I to this respond?
A shadow doth leave all splendor in want.
Lesser light doth eclipse a greater one
As doth the moon, not that the sun is not."

"Beloved, fleet doth resume the anxious glow
To rightful rule, the sun to its abode,
Reigneth to honor all it doth hallow.
Banish concern of a fading shadow."

(Excerpts from Shakespeare's Sonnets}
"To give away yourself keeps yourself still,
"And you must live, drawn by your own sweet skill." (XVL)

"But thy eternal summer shall not fade
Nor lose possession of that fair thou owest;
Nor shall Death brag thou wander'st in his shade..."
(XVIII)

"Didst not the sun at Jesus' cross withhold,
That holy God couldst not upon behold,
Who by Christ's blood, our sin debt wast revoked?
Dowry for his Bride Heaven's cost untold.

If all nor death sev'reth us, Christina,
There exists yet another enemy."
Her eyes delve into his, "My King, tell me!"
"Love that endureth not," he intimates.

He gently lifts the child up in his arms,
"Jerome, our little Prince, heaven's reward,
Created in the image of our God,
Having risen as we, saved from mortal harm.

We rose to life, love must not mortal be."
She weeps, "Undying love, I promise thee.
Idyll days, not few, chronicled shall be."
"My Queen, this love, I vow to him and thee."

War Announced to Krislos

Haslim, John, and Elaam stand at the door,
With them is their acquaintance, old Balfour.
Krislos, aware, requests to be informed.
"O King!" says Balfour, "Akaan stageth war!

Akaan hath ordered all his forces out,
To march in formation on Salem's route.
Horsemen, footmen, some four hundred thousand,
To make an assault on Salem throughout!"

Says Krislos, "I hear thee as credible,
And these three men trust thee, reliable.
Duke, withdrawal is inevitable,
Take our entourage to Berlbic's castle.

Take the Queen, child, Duchess, Julia, with thee,
Protected by thirty knights in the lead.
Take thy homing pigeons also with thee,
That worthy news, passing, may be received.

Haslim, first assemble a war council,
Apprise earls and dukedoms, make pronouncements,
Tell Berlbic of Akaan's soon encounter.
Salem, I'll address the crises mounting."

Krislos and Christina Part

He reenters the room with Christina,
"O my King, I've o'erheard the war's proceedings.
The entourage shall prepare for leaving."
Two servants enter the suite discreetly,

A chest, jewel work, arranged by the King,
A royal coronet, now for the Queen.
On her hand placed he a resplendent ring.
Say they 'Adieu,' and the King kisses the Queen.

With Krislos' letter, Milo in advance
Rides to tell Duke Berlbic the circumstance:
"The Queen flees from the war's envisioned path,
Expects Berlbic's patronage he will grant."

From the gate, John watches those departing,
Eyes and feelings linger, distance thwarting.
Shoals of crashing time with spoils, it harbors,
One standing as it ebbs cannot guard it.

Farewell to Christina, the child, Julia,
Duke Haslim and Duchess, six servants.
Milo, Victor, Celia,
Wagon masters, horses,
The two wolves, Coal and Pitch,
Homing pigeons.

Milo at Berlbic's Castle

Duke Berlbic, by a squire, is notified.
"Mercenary Milo waiteth outside."
The war hath commenced, Duke Berlbic surmised.
"Young Milo, fancy seeing thee arrive!

Not long since thou left, thou art back so soon?
Man, what hast thou to tell, is there war news?"
Milo says, "Akaan's troops art on the move,
Thou shall hear Duke Haslim, he is enroute."

Duke Berlbic replies, "Now thou say'st Haslim?"
"Sir, Haslim hath Krislos' plan of action,
The Duke with the Queen, fact of the matter."
"Krislos hath a Queen!? She, at my castle?"

"Aye, Queen Christina hath a newborn son,
And a fine prince he shall be, named Jerome."
Berlbic asks, "Is she worthy of the throne?"
Said Milo, "Dare say, she'd rule well alone!

She, quite esteemed, is worthy of the crown,
Remarkable beauty, engaging brow."
"Then," said the Duke, "a Queen's throne she shall have,
A splendid court for her station in pow'r.

Young Milo, is there more news I shouldst know?"
"Duke, the Queen hath her entourage, of course,
Her retinue of some twenty or more,
With thirty knights to serve our Queen adored."

Said Duke Berlbic, "I shouldst never have asked,
When will I see the Kingdom's other half?"
"Aye, Duke, thou hast a heart of gold. Alas,
Thou hast five days ere this cometh to pass."

Krislos' Address at Salem

The populace has word Krislos will speak.
All gather with leaders to hear the King.
At Salem's forum, they arrange to meet.
A thund'rous shout, "Hail King!" their voices ring.

"Welcome to thee, King Krislos!" The earth shook.
King Krislos, with his hands raised o'er them, stood.
Ere acclamations ceased, moments it took.
"Beloved sons and daughters of the Kingdom!

Today, we reunite, people and King.
Akaan wilt ne'er more plant his booted feet,
Stand in dominion, nor bring us defeat!"
"Hail to the King! Long live Krislos the King!"

"Akaan seized Salem on his first campaign,
Of his desire, a fraction of the claim.
He wageth war on Salem now again.
As for the throne, Krislos hath come to reign."

"Hail to the King!"

"God's foreknowledge and His power, sovereign,
With His hand to guide us, help is promised
To restore the Kingdom and our armies
By raising me to life, the harbinger.

The call to muster, every man must heed,
A man of war must every neighbor be.
Let not a coward make the warrior blink,
Every man be strong, all make strong the weak.

No heavier charge couldst weigh on our path,
Each man must take two others on his back,
Crushed kindred, fallen soldiers from attack,
Whilst for thyself, and country be not slack.

Migrate away thy folk far as ye can,
Hide and preserve food, each and every clan.
Portions of food, place in a poor man's hand,
That foes reap not, set fire to fields and land.

Beloved, paint the doorposts of thy homestead,
Remember the blood that thy kindred shed.
'Death angel, pass o'er us,' let it be said,
'Here we await our living, not our dead.'

We'll not lie down before our enemies.
We must take action immediately.
Do now what ye wouldst do eventually,
For if ye wait, there'll be no remedy.

Go ye brave soldiers to thy homes and farms,
Embrace thy wife and children in thine arms,
Let duty strive above a longing heart,
As thresholds hear thee say, 'I must depart.'

Muster in twelve days, may thy numbers grow.
Bring all weapons, though they be slings and stones,
We must take from the foe his well-strung bow,
Take then his sword, thy life deny the foe.

The new Kingdom shall live in glorious light,
Prosperity shall make its home with thine,
God's glory there, all homes shall magnify,
The hopeless, downcast on the knee, shall rise.

As the prophet Micah saith,
    'Rejoice not against me, O mine enemy,
    when I fall, I shall arise,
    when I sit in darkness,
    the Lord shall be a light unto me.' (Micah 7:8, KJV)

'God's righteousness from above looketh down.
Faithfulness looketh upward from the ground' (Psalm 85:11,
paraphrased)
"Let the stone at thy gate echo thy vow:
I shall return victorious, I shall!"

The War

Krislos calls the nation to prayer throughout.
John recollects Gideon, fleece laid out,
Three hundred put thousands of foes to rout. (Judges 7:7–8)
His faith in God brought vict'ry and renown.

The Invasion

Akkan strikes Salem with a massive force.
Aghast are Krislos' men, how vast they storm.
So loudly speak their woken battle horns,
They race here and there, mount the battle-horse.

With raven storm clouds preying overhead,
Krislos on Bolt O'Wrath rides fleet ahead
To wherein earth wooden stakes are embed.
There met foe's eyes unflinching, vehement red.

Ear-piercing horn blasts, deafening the roar,
Conflict, the iron-tipped enmity of war.
The firmament flinches as arrows soar,
Bow's deadly feud darkens the sky all the more.

A shower of arrows Krislos' men loosed,
Concert with lightning, bolts fierce they did shoot.
Akaan sees horror, carnage of his troops
Beneath battle shields, stricken warriors droop.

Both sides enter the maws of blackened night.
At Krislos' onslaught, shocked foes take to flight,
Pursuing at their heels are Bertrand's knights.
Well-traveled spears silence the wretched wights.

Akaan reverses course, turns back towards Pross,
His troops conflicted, clashing, running amok.
Mayhem's exchange, comrades each other fought.
Nature has made its descent upon the mob.

Battalions pocked with fright in disarray,
Aligned terror and panic, driving rage.
Trembling armor rattles with dread and quakes,
Horror intensifies, pulses in waves.

Each at the terrifying darkness swore,
The sword knows not its master nor its lord.
Ravenous for blood, pacified with gore,
Each man slashes his fellow with the same sword.

John's regiment advancing south has turned
Akaan's southern offensive to divert,
From Berlbic's contiguous realm avert,
Hence, the frenetic fury of John's spur.

The Queen's Orders to Haslim and Milo

Haslim and Milo heed the Queen's orders,
They bridle and saddle waiting horses.
Haslim whistles, his wolves keen to escort,
The men chart routes to scout upper borders.

The Duke and Milo, in seclusion, stay.
Listening, in the forest, they remain.
Alerted, thronged with anxious thoughts, they wait.
The sounds of surging horses come that way.

Antipathetic hordes sweep through the land,
Columns of foes, foot soldiers pushing past,
Haslim and Milo are caught in their path.
The lush forest bares its cover, alas.

The wolves burst out in defense of the two,
Exposing them to the enemy's full view.
"Milo! We die! There's nothing we can do!"
Milo is quickly captured, then the Duke.

Two soldiers stand before them with drawn swords.
"Lay down thy weapons now!" their captors warn.
Their swords drop with the weapons belts they wore.
The captain rides straight toward them on his horse.

"Who art ye?" he demands, impatiently,
"State thy names!" His eyes focus on Haslim.
"Haslim is my name" (now indignation).
"Haslim, Thief of Akaan's gold at Salem!

For Krislos, thou art spying on our troops!
The Sultan will have questions for ye soon.
Take them captive, they'll tell Krislos' next move."
The captors shout, "Forward, get ye afoot!"

For miles, the captives endure vile remarks.
With hands tied, they are compelled fast to march.
They hear the campaign of conflict afar,
The brutal strife, the savagery of war.

John and His Troop's Valorous Attack

John leads the zealous charge, fearless attack,
Face bold, spear staunchly held firm in his grasp.
Warhorses race with fury in their tracks,
Unwavering, John's forces face the clash.

The Sultan's eyes are fixed, Elaam's pursued,
Elaam flees wildly; passing John, he flew.
Instinctively, John's javelin is loosed,
Piercing the Sultan's chest, the spear ran through.

Officers spin around in disbelief,
He fell to the shock of the Sultan's men,
Down from his warhorse, from his regency.
"Give Bozran aid, repel the enemy!"

Relentless scourge, the epic arrows swarm.
Hot vengeful missiles fast from quivers drawn.
Torrid, as well, the javelins are launched,
The horrid weapons shrieked, "Slaughter John!"

John lies upon the fateful soil, face up.
One, flush full of rancor, standing above,
With all brute force, his aimed weapon is thrust.
The flashing spear brings forth John's gushing blood.

Elaam glances at John's horrific plight,
He bolts, hurtling toward John to save his life,
Grabs a battle axe, cleaves with all his might,
Lays open the assailant, gruesome sight.

Elaam, beside him, tends to John near death,
Stymies the rushing blood by wounds compressed.
John's shield caught fifty arrows, embedded.
Haslim and Milo incredulous, distressed.

John's horse, too, was brought down, courageous beast,
Endured the scorching torrent, battle heat,
Devoted horse, at war, defied defeat.
Duty prevailed unto the final feat.

Midst the crazed conflict, evermore intense,
John is borne on a litter to a tent.
Eventually, the day's fight draws to an end.
To notify the Queen, word must be sent.

The Tent

The tent is readied, wherein John is laid,
His armor and bloody clothing stripped away.
With a flagon of water, wounds are bathed.
To tell the Queen, Milo goes for her sake.

A small lamp flickers o'er John's hapless head,
Forestalling shadows, anxiousness, and dread,
The heir of every breath passed to the next,
The monitored condition of each breath.

After a day, till the approaching night,
The Queen, her carriage, retinue, and knights,
Her priest, physician, and Julia there arrive
Bringing lamps to the tent for fitting light.

Wolves, Coal and Pitch, lie whimp'ring at John's feet.
Julia, left side, sits, to his right, the Queen.
Mere signs of life, ere anguished eyes would see.
Christina takes John's hand and softly speaks,

"Doth sworn valor deserve so rich a wound?
Nourished wast a prince from thy mother's womb.
For Elaam thou didst face death, staunch pursuit,
With mettle envied by my first rescue.

John, thou my prince," with her voice, quavering,
"Thou lackest the anointing of a King."
Whether Christina heard, or so it seemed,
Last breath he faintly spoke, "Farewell my Queen."

The physician spoke the final unction,
Christina cries, "John!" in vain she summons.
Sorrows pour with many tears aflooding,
Inconsolable, her loss ere sudden.

"Many waters cannot quench love;
rivers cannot wash it away
...for love is strong as death." (Song of Songs 8:6-7 NIV)

The Priest bows his head, as do Haslim, Elaam, and Milo.
He prays,
"We know that if this earthly tent that is
our body is destroyed, we have a tabernacle
from God...eternal in the heavens,
for in this tent we groan..." (2 Cor 5:1–2 NKJV)

Julia mourns, "This doth steal last words away,
Thy brighter hopes purchased too harsh a fate.
I wast too vain to allow thine embrace,
How canst my fault be quenched, love spoken late."

War De-escalates

Enemies separate, each to their own.
Near noiseless torpor in the land of foes.
Whom will lead, or whom to obey? None knows.
Seems stolid warriors bring war to a close.

The Queen Meets the Troops

Soldiers surround the tent to learn of John.
The Queen's presence signifies a grim outcome.
With this apprehension, the men have come.
The Queen steps out to these troops in despond.

"Hail to the Queen!"

"Brave soldiers, God help ye, thy leader died."
The men's hearts sink, hearing of John's demise.
"He gave his all, his life he sacrificed.
We shall fight for our Kingdom to survive!

War's pitiless breath speaketh against life.
John wouldst have ye to live and not to die.
We must win battles with courageous might,
We must follow King Krislos to the fight."
"Be strong, and let us fight bravely for our people
and the cities of our God."(1 Chron. 19:13, NIV)

"Let us at all costs aid our wounded men.
I shall not leave till we to this attend.
Thereafter ye shall stand in Berlbic's realm,
King Krislos shall command ye from that end."

Jerome Taken Hostage

The Queen is interrupted as she talks,
A knight racing toward them abruptly halts,
"O Queen! Throughout the land, thou hast been sought!
The Chamberlain who sent me is distraught.

Thy son Jerome hath been kidnapped!" She screams.
"For hostage, the men hadst first sought for thee!
By Providence, they couldst not find the Queen,
So Victor pledged Jerome in lieu of thee!

The Duchess, confronting, wast pushed away."
The Queen cried, "Why didst I not measures take?
There were too few safeguards to keep him safe."
She weeps with much regret for her mistake.

She wails, "I may not see my son again!
A ransom Akaan surely wilt demand.
Between Kings, this matter will be addressed.
Inform King Krislos now, in haste, Haslim!"

If there must be war,
Let the heart last enter,
But the heart defend foremost.

John's Funeral

The drear procession, led by King and Queen,
Their royal carriage coursed along the green,
John's solemn funeral cortege is seen,
Ne'er would Hector have thought of John deceased.

He holds in one hand reins of Bolt O'Wrath,
And in the other, John's escutcheon's grasped,
White stallion draped with black silk mantelet,
Led with no mounted warrior on its back.

Behold, John's shield aloft in Hector's hand,
Wherein the fifty arrows fraught did hang,
John fallen, stoutly stood, a kingly man,
Lavish his blood, incomparable his stand.

The bier in the procession, portage slow,
White myrtle garlands sanctify its cloak.
The priest crying the elegy bespoke,
"Alas, the Lion! Alas, the Hero!" *(The Life and
Times of Jesus, pg. 555)*

Where is the shroud now for Ariel's sake?
"God, lengthen my days," Hezekiah prayed,
"Lo, what God giveth, sovereign God canst take,
That God numb'reth our days, His Book doth say."

The plaintive strain of Julia's flute connotes
Lament amidst God's Spirit to console,
As cymbals, melancholy, accents low,
Address the psyches of the sad of soul.

The priest officiating at the grave,
"Wars on the earth, nor death shall e'er abate.
Death respecteth no man, and none escape.
In Christ, in the Last Day, John shall be raised."

Ransom

"For ransom, Akaan demandeth Elaam,
No surprise," says Krislos, "but imminent."
Christina, wincing, shows her sentiment,
"This is tantamount to the death sentence."

Elaam, of noble heart, with compassion,
"I shall go for the child to be ransomed."
Krislos stunned, "Art thou sure of such action?"
"O King, doubtless, 'tis audacious, drastic.

Otherwise, if for rescue, troops art sent,
The child's life wouldst be risked, as well thy men.
The conscience of the populace offend.
'Twas Akaan's own son he didst apprehend."

He laments, "I have brought this upon us."
"And how so?" Christina asks, astonished.
"All of Akaan's gold I took, absconding.
King Akaan, shrewdly plotting, responded."

Elaam adds, "If Jerome is not ransomed,
Akaan shall raise the boy while he's nascent,
As Janissary, which Akaan sanctioneth,
Jerome's chance of knowing thy God, is abandoned.

He'll learn thou art a foe he must depose.
He wouldst as soon slay thee as any foe."
Christina held back tears, as Elaam spoke,
"O who wilt rescue thee? May God do so!"

Christina says, "Thou hast rescued me twice,
The first, at Salem, though risking thy life,
Freed me from vile men, their wicked designs,
Thou didst come forth bloody, barely alive.

Again, enabling my rescue at Pross,
Thou didst chance life, forfeiting high office,
One rescue more I wilt mention, my 'cross,'
Thou didst take from the thief to stem my loss,

Fitting that I give thee my cross and due,
A debt I owe, sincerest gratitude.
Unselfish sacrifice thy deeds have proved,
Done so with dignity, divine virtue."

"Gracious Queen," Elaam responds, deeply moved,
"If what thou say'st doth constitute virtue,
It doth the more hearten one to rescue,
As heaven's ransom of souls doth presume."

Ransom Officials Received

Akaan's ransom officials are received
By Krislos for the exchange to proceed.
"We have, in faith, brought forth the Prince to thee,
Now release Elaam to us as agreed."

Holding the child, Celia stands by Victor.
Christina rushes out to seize the boy,
Drawing him close, embracing all the more,
Ecstatic he's been rescued, overjoyed.

Pathos manifests on King Krislos' face,
He thought he'd capitulated in this case,
Suspects Akaan is acting in bad faith.
Krislos groans, "Vale" Elaam's whisked away.

 Late, the Queen rushes to Krislos' chamber,
Alarmed, distraught, tearful, with rare anger.
"My Queen! What upseteth thee?" he asks her.
"The child is not my son!" starkly answered.

"The evidence, he is not circumcised,
Though quite Jerome's image, he's not my child!
Vile Victor thought he couldst save his own hide,
By perpetrating this foul deed with guile!"

Krislos, seething, rises to his feet, wroth.
"This cursed treachery wast all hatched at Pross.
A conspiracy Victor helped to plot!
Gaoler! To the court, have Victor brought!"

Victor at Trial

Victor's cell is unlocked, day is breaking.
"Victor, prepare thyself to face the King!"
Under gaoler's watch, Victor shaking,
Standing now in court nervously waiting.

Krislos states, "Victor, thou dost face charges:
Thou art charged with treason, kidnapping, fraud.
The child is not the Queen's son, thou hast brought,
But a likeness, fruit of thy search at Pross!

Victor, state thy case, speak in thy defense."
"O King, under duress, these things I didst,
I fought kidnappers, protected the Prince,"
Krislos says, "This doth dispute evidence.

Men came to seize the Queen for ransom use,
They failed, thou didst proffer the Prince in lieu.
Thou didst travel to Pross to disabuse
The least doubt he is Akaan's son, in truth,

That thou wouldst gain reward like none other.
To save thy skin, thou sought Jerome's double.
Akaan couldst keep Jerome, stage the other,
Thus, cunningly deceive the Queen Mother.

Victor, I sentence thee to prison main.
Gaoler, hold Victor in bonds and chains.
As Elaam's treatment is, whilst he's detained,
Victor's wilt so be meted out the same."

Krislos Reunites with Former Army

Eager to meet the requirements for the troops,
Berlbic worked diligently to recruit
Men who once served Krislos with fortitude.
Significantly, numbers have improved.

The known commanders unite with their men,
They gather once again and reminisce,
Camaraderie around campfires and tents,
They talk of war, of threats and enemies.

They coalesce around Krislos again,
They hear his strategy, what he has planned,
His war resolve, to make a full advance,
Conquer, occupy Pross, to rule the land.

"Hail King Krislos, long live the King!" they shout.
Krislos, spirits high, emboldened, speaks out,
"Ye brave men have returned to fight this hour.
Ye, like no other fighting force or pow'r.

The javelin that took thy leader's life,
We shall hurl back and strike with all our might!
That sworn swift blade wilt conquer and divide.
Polish thy swords, on vic'try keep thine eye!"

"Hail to the King!"

Krislos Advances War

Akaan boasts, outwitting Krislos, amused.
"Exceedingly artful beyond dispute.
Two birds Akaan didst snare with but one ruse,
The Prince and the Emir," he cites the news.

Akaan has the five Princes seated near.
"Toast, lift the cup to what shall soon appear,
Our treasury, stolen by the Emir,
And to my Prince who's now residing here.

Be merry now, do homage to desire,
Drink up and dine, sate ye thine appetite,
What's overdue with passion's full delights,
Much revelry with minstrelsy, sweet wine."

Drunken orgies continue day and night,
Indulgence keeps the harems occupied,
While Krislos' troops are storming now in sight,
For war Akaan is ill prepared to fight.

Akaan's Quarters Disclosed

Akaan keeps Jerome safe in concealment,
Aiding in care are Anne and Maria.
These former servants have not seen Elaam,
Nor will they be permitted to see him.

Since Akaan's destruction of the abbey,
The Abbot has been held at Pross captive.
Akaan's penchant for the shroud emphatic,
He has the shroud near with ready access.

Rapt dreams of Akaan seem to be frequent,
Less understood vicissitudes of sleep,
Suspected is the shroud's proximity,
Prompting aberrations, visions, and dreams.

One early morn, Akaan summons Ambrose.
The King, in a quandary, his face shows,
An enigmatic gaze the King's eyes hold.
"O King," he asks, "What doth disturb thee so?"

"I dreamt One radi'nt in white vesture stood,
Eyes blazed like fire, his head and hair like wool, (Rev. 1:14)
His sash scribed: 'WORD OF GOD, FAITHFUL AND TRUE.'
(Rev. 19:11)
'Akaan, God loveth thee.' "Those words ensued."

Akaan asks, "What is this dream, this omen?
I do not comprehend love of this One.
The monastery and the Books Holy
I burned. Thou, by chance, saved the shroud only."

Perplexed, Akaan recites, "He spake my name,
Although I know not this person who came."
Ambrose, convinced, "Tis like what others claim,
'Twas Jesus, sinless Son of God who came,"

Ambrose Unfolds the Shroud for King Akaan
'Jesus' hands and feet to a cross impaled, (Psalm 22:16-18;
Mark 15:24)
Bore our sins in his own body, availed. (1 Peter 2:24)
"Behold the stains of blood caused by the nails,
His sinless sacrifice o'er sin prevailed.

"Thou dost not know Jesus," Ambrose clarifies,

    "'The Word was made flesh and lived for a while among
    us. We have seen his glory, the glory of the one and only
    Son,who came from the Father, full of grace and truth."
    (John 1:14) NIV
    'But now he has appeared once for all at the end of the
    ages to do away with sin by the sacrifice of himself.'"
    (Heb 9:26) NIV

Akaan asks, "Jesus sacrificed? Why him?"
Ambrose answers,

    "Because Jesus is Son of God and Son of Man. (Acts 7:56; Lk.
    18:31;Mt. 24:27)
    Sacrificial blood of the Son of Man, (Heb. 9:14)
    For sin's remission, only His blood can. (Heb. 9:22b)
    Sinless Son of God, Holy God demands." (Heb. 1:5-9;
    Mt. 3:17; Mt. 16:16)

    'the blood of Christ, who through the eternal Spirit
    offered himself unblemished to God.' (Heb 9:14) NIV
    '...and without shedding of blood is no forgiveness.'
    (Heb. 9:22b) NIV
    'God made him who had no sin to be sin for us,
    so that in him we might become the righteousness of
    God '" (2 Cor. 5:21) NIV

Akaan, engrossed in what Ambrose saith,
From the prophet's word, book of Isaiah,
The Son must suffer and die as Messiah,
Jesus atoned for our sins to save us."

Akaan asks, "Can God die?"

Ambrose tells him,

> "Though Jesus died to atone for our sins, (Lk 24:46 NIV)
> As God's son, death couldst not remain in Him,
> (Rom. 6:10) NIV
> the 'resurrection and the life,' He is." (John 11:25) NIV

> 'For we know that since Christ was raised from the dead,
> he cannot die again; death no longer has mastery over
> him. (Rom. 6:9) NIV
> 'For as the Father has life in himself, so he has granted the
> Son to have life in himself.' (John. 5:26) NIV

> '...but it has now been revealed through the appearing of
> our Savior, Christ Jesus, who has destroyed death and has
> brought life and immortality to light through the gospel.
> (2 Tim. 1:10) NIV

> Jesus said, "'I tell you the truth, whoever hears my word
> and believes him who sent me has eternal life and will not
> be condemned; he has crossed over from death to life.'"
> (John. 5:24) NIV

> "'Jesus Christ, the Righteous One, he is the atoning
> sacrifice for our sins, and not only for ours, but also for
> the sins of the whole world...'" (1 John 2:2) NIV

> "'that God was reconciling the world to himself in
> Christ, not counting men's sins against them. And he has
> committed to us the message of reconciliation.'" (2 Cor
> 5:19) NIV

"In the beginning God created man innocent of sin.

God formed Adam from dust, the first man made.
When man wast formed, God held but lifeless clay.
God breathed into Adam's nostrils, breath he gave. (Gen 2:7)
A living soul, in God's image, God made. (Gen 1:26, 27)

Adam sinned, forsook God's holy image, (Gen. 3:5,6)
Sin reigned and spread throughout the human race:
(Rom 5:18)
Man, dead in sin and transgressions, became, (Eph 2:1)
Helpless as dust, his soul in lifeless state. (Gen 2:17)

As God's word doth say, 'The soul that sinneth it shall die.' (Ez.
18:20) KJ

'For as in Adam all die, even so in Christ shall all be made
alive.'"(1 Cor 15:22) KJ

Akaan unbowed protests, "I am not dead!
My strength doth abound above strongest tests,
My wit and capabilities attest."
"O King, consider Adam," Ambrose said.

'For all have sinned and come short of the glory of God.'
(Rom. 3:23) KJ

'As for you, you were dead in your transgressions and sins,
...we were by nature objects of wrath. But because of his
great love for us, God...made us alive with Christ even
when we were dead in transgressions. (Eph. 2:1, 3, 4) NIV

'For the law of the Spirit of life in Christ Jesus
hath made me free from the law of sin and death.'
(Rom 8:2) KJ
'Predestined to be conformed to the image of his Son.' (Rom
8:29) KJ
'Who is the image of the invisible God..." (Col 1:15a) KJ

'And just as we have borne the image of the man of dust,
we shall also bear the image of the man of heaven.' (1 Cor.
15:49) ESV

'Jesus said, "The Spirit gives life; the flesh counts for
nothing. The words I have spoken to you, are spirit and they
are life.'" (John 6:63) NIV
The Spirit himself testifies with our spirit that we God's
children.' (Rom. 8:16) NIV

"Christ came to bring life to our souls, thou seest?
Thou must see thy soul apart from thy strength.
In Christ one's soul liveth eternally.
And without Christ, thou canst not live O King.

Christ must breathe the Holy Spirit into thee for eternal life."
    Jesus said, 'That which is born of flesh is flesh;
    and that which is born of Spirit is spirit.' (John 3:6) KJ

    Verily, verily, I say unto thee, Except a man be born again,
    he cannot see the kingdom of God' (John 3:3) KJ
    'He that hath the Son hath life;
    And he that hath not the Son hath not life.' (1John 5:12) KJ

'I am the way, the truth, and the life; no man
cometh unto the Father, but by me.' (John 14:6) KJ

"Ambrose, Jesus wouldst die for my sins. Why?"

Ambrose explains,
"That thou in thy sins wouldst not have to die. (John 8:24)
Unto men, once to die, it is assigned.(Heb 9:27)
After death, to judgment one is consigned.

'For the wages of sin is death, but the gift of God
is eternal life through Jesus Christ our Lord.'
(Rom 6:23) KJ
'For God so loved the world, that He gave his only
begotten Son, that whosoever believeth in him should not
perish, but have everlasting life.' (John 3:16) KJ

'For there is one God, and one mediator between God and
men, the man Christ Jesus.' Who gave himself as a ransom
for all men...(1 Tim 2:5,6a) KJ
'Wherefore God also hath highly
exalted him, and given him a name
which is above every name:
That at the name of Jesus every knee
should bow, of things in heaven, and
things in earth, and things under the earth;
And that every tongue should confess that
Jesus Christ is Lord, to the glory of God the
Father.' (Phil. 2:9-11) KJ

'Neither is there salvation in any other: for there is
none other name under heaven given among men,
whereby we must be saved.' (Acts 4:12) KJ

Jesus said, 'Enter ye in at the strait gate:
for wide is the gate, and broad is the way,
that leadeth to destruction, and many there be
which go in thereat; Because strait is the gate,
and narrow is the way, which leadeth unto life,
and few there be that find it.' (Matt 7:13, 14) KJ

'The Lord...is longsuffering toward us, not willing
that any should perish, but that all should come to
repentance." (2 Peter 3:9) KJ

For God sent not his Son into the world to condemn the
world; But that the world through him might be saved.
He that believeth on him is not condemned; but he that
believeth not is condemned already, because he hath not
believed in the name of the only begotten Son of God.
(Jn. 3:17,18) KJ

"O King, "seek the Lord while He may be found;
call upon Him while He is near.
Let the wicked forsake his way
...for He will abundantly pardon.' (Isa 55:6-7) KJ

'Everyone who confesses the name of the Lord
must turn away from wickedness.'" (2 Tim 2:19b) NIV

Akaan asks him, "What must I do, Ambrose,
to obtain eternal life for my soul?"

"Eternal life is not obtained, O King,
By good works nor honorable deeds,
By personal goodness as one thinks,
Lest anyone boast about such things."

'It is the gift of God, not as of works,
Lest any man should boast.' (Eph 2:9) KJ
'For by grace are ye saved through faith,
  and that not of yourselves...'(Eph. 2:8

"'That if thou shalt confess with thy mouth
the Lord Jesus, and shalt believe in thine heart
that God hath raised him from the dead, thou shalt be
saved.' (Rom. 10:9) KJ

'For with the heart man believeth unto,
righteousness;. and with the mouth confession
is made unto salvation.'" (Rom 10:10) KJV

By faith, personally trust Christ," said Ambrose.
"Jesus as Savior and Lord thou must know."

Akaan bows humbly, asking God to forgive him of his sins,
and prays for Jesus to come into his heart that he may know
Christ and have eternal life.

Akaan proclaims,
"I shall call Jesus 'Lord', Son of God, my Savior and my God."

Ambrose, affirming, "O King, blessed art thou, blessings be
upon thee."

> 'All we like sheep have gone astray; we have turned every
> one to his own way; and the Lord hath laid on him the
> iniquity of us all' (Isa. 53:6) KJ
> '...by his knowledge shall my righteous servant justify
> many; for he shall bear their iniquities.' (Isa. 53:11b) KJ
> 'But he was wounded for our transgressions, he was
> bruised for our iniquities; the chastisement of our peace
> was upon him; and with his stripes we are healed.'
> (Isa 53:5) KJ

The End of War

Akaan's Surrender

Krislos' armed forces have triumphed at Pross,
Sometime after final warfare was launched.
All the dead have been buried with honor,
Be they ally or enemy losses.

Krislos and Akaan Meet

"King Akaan, thou shall meet King Krislos now."

Akaan quips, "Ah, an inquisition now!
Under the scrutiny of Krislos' brow,
To hear adjudication from his mouth.
O how unskilled fate doth distinguish crowns."

Akaan enters wearing a royal robe,
As dignity does his station connote.
Krislos, regarding one lately deposed,
Stands for the one in war he has opposed.

"Is it thou King Krislos, mine avenger,
Who hath come to punish the offender?
Or hath come to hear the word, 'Surrender?'
To King Jesus I've declared submission."

Incredulity o'er Krislos' face shone.
"Thou needest no other King but Christ alone.
Surrender to God giveth peace to souls,
Surrender, thou must, for peace with Krislos.

Akaan, now bring the child Jerome, forthwith.
I shall see Emir Elaam after this."
Akaan perspires, trepidation within,
Timorously, he has the child brought in.

Krislos carefully views his face and form.
Jerome's demeanor displays weal and warmth.
Krislos must be impartial at this point.
"Dost thou love this child or is he a pawn?

If a pawn, then state thy case to Krislos,
If thou hast deep paternal love, say so."
Akaan trembles, "I pray thee, King, Krislos,
Take not away from me, my son Jerome."

Krislos torn, sees Christina's loss the same.
What would Solomon decide if he spake?
"Oh heavenly Father, hear," Krislos prays,
"Thy will be done, upon Thee we shall wait."

"This matter of thy son, wait thou to hear;
My charge now fulfill; bring in the Emir."
Akaan falters, "Soon Elaam shall be here,
Some preparation is needed, I fear."

In the cell, Elaam lies still, enervate.
He has been subjected to starvation
Till he tells the treasury's location.
The guard jogs Elaam, there's no reaction.

Then he slaps Elaam, there's no sign of breath.
With certainty that the Emir is dead,
The guard scrambles to report; the news spreads.
Krislos receives the word that he most dreads.

Krislos orders the Abbot, "Bring the shroud!
Elaam is dead, pray now to God!" he shouts.
"In faith to God, Ambrose, we must cry out!
Akaan, pray to Jesus!" Akaan kneels down.

The shroud held heavenward then is laid o'er.
Covering the body,. Krislos implores,
"In Jesus name, Emir Elaam, come forth!"
His body lies motionless, a mere corpse.

Veins in Elaam's corpse start to recompose.
His limbs regain form, his head and torso.
His face regenerates likeness also.
Convulsively he heaves, coughs, eyes emote.

"Servants! Bring food and water quickly, rush!"
Overjoyed, Krislos helps Elaam sit up.
Only on the food Elaam's eyes focus,
Of those standing around he's not conscious.

He chokes on food from gulping and quaffing.
Several minutes pass, he hears talking,
Elaam turns his head around awkwardly.
He sees Krislos and others there watching.

His slow eyes rest on Maria and Anne,
Faint recall takes him back to Salem's camp,
Where they beheld his deadly wounds, aghast.
The women thought to save his life, their task.

Jerome is held securely in Anne's arms.
Elaam's focus on them thus corresponds,
The child's arms reach out to Elaam fondly,
While Anne sees Krislos' amiable nod.

Elaam's attention growing more in phase,
Jerome's hand reaches up to Elaam's face.
To everyone's delight, Elaam relates.
All watch as Elaam's hand on his is placed.

Elaam's burden of weakness encumbers,
Weariness beckons him to deep slumber.
To resume care for Jerome, Anne's summoned.
Akaan's new life in Christ, the true wonder.

The Treaty of Surrender at Pross

Surreal the moment, predicted none would,
As two kings bowing to each other could.
The terms of surrender now understood.
The treaty, paradox of nations, stood.

SALEM'S GATE

OF VICTORY

Krislos Addresses His Troops

Krislos signals his troops, familiar horn.
Battalions stand in their respective form.
Officers beside him in uniform,
Krislos addresses them from high platform.

    "Brave men of Salem,
    A proud king and naiton salute ye.

Salem giveth gratitude to each man.
Those in graves we honor, their honor stands.
The Emir shall supplant and rule this land.
Akaan shall be a figurehead at hand."

"Hail to the King!" they shout vivaciously.
"Akaan surrendered uncondition'lly!
We shall occupy Pross, rare victory!
Ye have suffered much but made history!

Salem shall prosper well in the Kingdom,
Great rejoicing in the land there shall be.
Return ye to thy homes and families,
Rejoin those who with longing await ye!

In our land shall be great celebrations,
The King and Queen's marriage consummation,
And all shall behold her coronation."
"Long live the King and Queen of our nation!"

The King Returns Victorious

Majestic Bolt O' Wrath revels in proud prance.

The King rides high astride his white stallion,
Elaam, Milo next lead the battalions.
 Folk rush toward the trumpet sound protracted,
A pressing call to which they're attracted.

The trumpet sounds, its loud summit lasting,
Duke and Duchess harken at the castle.
Hector is aware of the happening.,
Thunderous signal, all leap, reacting.

"Our King victorious saves our nation!"
The people hail troops with wild elation,
Honor officers, horsemen parading.
As many columns of troops march trailing.

After King Krislos' and troop's pageantry,
A glorious view all anticipate,
The King and Queen appear with majesty,
They marvel at the people's happiness.

For the King and Queen's royal reception
At Salem, unequaled preparation.
The castle's great hall without exception,
Its splendor exceeds all expectations.

Artisans, makers of Christina's crown,
Crucibles' gold nectar, purest, renowned.
Molten glow doth rush to mold's hallowed ground.
Intricate halo, orb'd to fashion round.

The Heraldist cries before the nation:
"Our queen, Christina, her coronation.
On her the royal diadem is placed.
With such a crown as this, Christ's Bride shall reign!"

On flower-strewn pavements joyous dancing,
Clapping of hands with singing and gladness.
Young women rejoice with their tambourines,
Others with pipes and instruments with strings.

Veneration of the King and Queen

The crowd's exuberance is unending,
Rich gifts to the King and Queen, yet sending,
Bestowing many tributes commending,
They cry, "Peace with thee!" voices transcending.

A great hush, silence, Akaan with his son,
Entering, he assists the little one.
Bearing a gift to the Queen, the child comes.
The shroud, with Akaan's help, he holds as such.

The small child to whom she gave birth looks up,
"My gift to thee, Mother." Her tears well up.
She kneels, her heart races with Jerome's touch.
"Thou art my gift! God's gift, my precious son."

King Krislos hails, "King Akaan, my brother!
Thou art bidden to the wedding supper!"
"Aye, King Krislos, let us feast together.
In the Kingdom, let peace reign forever."

The Bride beams, glowing with radiant face.
The lamps are raised, the Bride's beauty is praised.
Along with the King, passing through the gate,
Those in the wedding procession await.

"This is the gate of the Lord, the righteous shall enter
through it." (Ps. 118:20) ESV

Marriage Supper of the Lamb

"Let us be glad and rejoice, and give honor to him,
for the marriage of the Lamb is come,
and his wife hath made herself ready."
"And to her was granted that she should be arrayed in
fine linen,
clean and white: for the fine linen is the righteousness
of saints."
...Blessed are they which are called unto the marriage supper
of the Lamb..."
"And I saw heaven opened, and behold a white horse;
and he that sat upon him was called 'Faithful and True',
and in righteousness he doth judge and make war."
His eyes were as a flame of fire,
and on his head were many crowns..."
And he was clothed with a vesture dipped in blood;
and his name is called 'The Word of God.'"

And he hath on his vesture and on his thigh a name written:
'KING OF KINGS, AND LORD OF LORDS.' (Rev.19:7–9,11–13,16)
KJ

The Bride

'Thou shalt also be a crown of glory in the hand of the LORD,
And a royal diadem in the hand of thy God.
Thou shalt no more be termed Forsaken;
neither shall thy land any more be termed Desolate:...'
...for the LORD delighteth in thee,
and thy land shall be married.
For as a young man marrieth a virgin,
so shall my sons marry thee:
And as the bridegroom rejoiceth over the bride,
so shall thy God rejoice over thee.' (Isa 62:3–5) NASB

'And the king will desire your beauty.
Since he is your lord, bow to him.
All glorious is the princess in her chamber,
with robes interwoven with gold.
In many-colored robes she is led to the King,
with her virgin companions following behind her.
(Psalm 45:11, 13, 14, ESV)
Your robes are all fragrant with myrrh and aloes and cassia.'
'From ivory palaces, stringed instruments make you glad.'
(Psalm 45:8, ESV)

THE END

Bibliography

Edersheim, Alfred. *The Life and Times of Jesus the Messiah.* (*"Alas, the lion! Alas, the hero!)* *p. 555,* New One Volume Edition, William B. Eerdmans Publishing Company. Grand Rapids, MI, 1974.

Drachmann, Holger, *Classic Sea Stories,* (*"I am contented with my store,* Altho' I should not be the worse *For just a little more."),* p. 602, Barry Unsworth, London, Leopard, a division of Random House, 20 Vauxhall Bridge Road, London, 1996.

Spurgeon, C.H., Morning and Evening. ("Behold the Emperor of Woe...gaze into His wounds and heal our own."), p. 409, Hendrickson Publishers, Inc., Carol Stream, IL, 1991.

Neil, William, *Concise Dictionary of Religious Quotations,* Nathan Soderblom Life, (*"Only with God's good hand and strict bridle can the soul be helped to give its best."*) p. 66. Thomas A Kempis, (*"Love feels no burden, thinks nothing of trouble, attempts what is above its strength...where he who does not love, would faint and lie down."*) p. 113, William B. Eerdmans Publishing Company, Grand Rapids, MI., 1974.

English Standard Version, (ESV), The Holy Bible Copyright 2008 by Crossway